Transforming Krodha

With kind regards, ॐ and prem

Swami Niranjan

Transforming Krodha

Swami Ratnashakti Saraswati

Under the Guidance of
Swami Niranjanananda Saraswati

Yoga Publications Trust, Munger, Bihar, India

Published by Yoga Publications Trust
    First edition 2019

ISBN: 978-81-940805-2-7

Publisher and distributor: Yoga Publications Trust, Ganga Darshan, Munger, Bihar, India.

Website: www.biharyoga.net

Printed at Thomson Press (India) Limited, New Delhi, 110001

Dedication

*In humility we offer this dedication to
Swami Sivananda Saraswati, who initiated
Swami Satyananda Saraswati into the secrets of yoga.*

Managing the Six Conditions

Swami Niranjanananda Saraswati

Our entire life we are dealing with one element, the mind. For every learning, every achievement and action we use the help of this great power called the mind. Manas, buddhi, chitta and ahamkara are the four aspects that constitute the whole mind. There is also a nature in the mind which is influenced by the senses, the *karmendriyas* and the *jnanendriyas*, organs of action and organs of perception. Everybody thinks of manas, buddhi, chitta, ahamakara, yet beyond this classification is the nature of mind.

From the perspectives of tantra, yoga, Vedanta and Samkhya, the mind is coloured by the three gunas – sattwa, rajas and tamas which represent the condition and the influence under which the mind functions. If the mind is under the tamasic influence, every response, thought and pattern of action and behaviour will be tamasic. If the mind is under the rajasic influence, everything will be rajasic. If the mind is under the influence of sattwa, everything will be sattwic, positive, uplifting and inspirational.

Every spiritual tradition teaches us how to manage and transform the negatives, the conditions of tamoguna and rajoguna. The moment people look at the nature of the mind, they find it difficult to accept that they are negative. Therefore, everybody looks at the classification of the mind and nobody looks at the *swabhava* of the mind, the nature and behaviour of the mind. This is an important aspect of becoming a yoga sadhaka, managing the conditions of the mind and recognizing the barriers which stop your progress. Don't live in a world of imagination and fantasy, instead see what stops you, what the blockages are and how you can overcome them. Once you are able to manage your tamoguna, you will attain sattwa. Enlightenment is something which you achieve when you have overcome the six conditions of mind which hold you grounded to this dimension and plane; and that is the final challenge.

There are six basic conditions in the mind which are coloured by the gunas: *kama, krodha, lobha, moha, mada, matsarya,* desire, anger, greed, infatuation, arrogance and envy. They become the cause of your discontentment and dissatisfactions in life. Everything in your life and in your mind rotates along these six conditions. In the Indian tradition, these six have been called by many names. Some call them the *shatripu* or the six enemies which ensure that the human mind is confined to this gross dimension and do not allow it to be awakened. Some people call them the six friends.

I have called them six friends for they are with us right from birth. They are an integral part of how we think, how we act, live and behave. They are conditions which life receives in which it has to develop, grow and evolve. Similarly, in order to evolve spiritually the six conditions have to be dealt with and managed. This is an important part of the yogic sadhana.

Contents

The 2nd Chapter of Yoga

Sri Swami Satyananda Saraswati established the Bihar School of Yoga in 1963, in order to fulfil the mandate of his guru, Swami Sivananda Saraswati. The mandate Swami Satyananda received was to propagate the science of yoga and take yoga from "shore to shore and door to door". In the days of Swami Sivananda, yoga was far from the globally recognized and accepted word it is today. Yoga was considered a spiritual practice reserved for sannyasins and renuniciates who had renounced society and were seeking enlightenment. It was not seen as something that could be incorporated into society and practised by the general public.

When the Bihar School of Yoga was established, the philosophy, practices, applications and lifestyle of yoga as practical and scientific systems were unknown, even in Indian society. From the beginning, yoga training and propagation by the Bihar School of Yoga took the form of intensive residential programs, in which yoga was taught as a way to qualitatively enhance physical health, mental peace, emotional harmony. A sequence of progression in yoga was defined fifty years ago by Swami Satyananda, by giving systematic training first in hatha yoga, raja yoga, and kriya yoga, as *bahiranga yoga*, external yoga. Simultaneously, training in *antaranga*, internal, aspect of karma yoga, bhakti and jnana yoga was provided through the lifestyle and inspiration of the ashram environment. A holistic or integral yoga system developed in which the yoga aspirant could awaken and integrate the faculties of head, heart and hands. The different *angas*, limbs, of yoga become the means of attaining this personal harmony and integrated expression.

In the early 1940s, the subject of yoga was propagated across the world by teachers and masters of different traditions, introducing the idea that through the practice of yoga one could explore the body, mind, emotions, and have a glimpse into one's spiritual nature. The first-generation teachers focused on bringing the knowledge of yoga to human society according to the need of the society at that time. In the 1960s, yoga was seen as a physical culture. In the 1970s, it was seen as a way to overcome stress, anxiety, tension and to improve the physical and mental functions. In the 1980s, research into the various possibilities and potentials of yoga to assist and promote physical and mental health took the forefront. By the 1990s, a rapid increase in the popularity of the practice of asana was evident across the globe. The asana component of yoga had been accepted worldwide and other components of yoga were relegated to the background and largely ignored by the mainstream practitioners and majority of yoga teachers. Today, 28 million people are practising yoga in the United States alone and statistics estimate 300 million practitioners worldwide.

In 2013, the World Yoga Convention was conducted in Munger to celebrate the Golden Jubilee of the Bihar School of Yoga. Over 50,000 yoga practitioners, teachers, students and aspirants participated in this historic event either in person or through the internet. The Convention was a milestone that marked the completion of fifty years of yoga propagation. The mandate of taking yoga from shore to shore and door to door was fulfilled. Over a fifty-year period, with the help of yoga aspirants and well-wishers all over the world, a yogic renaissance had taken place. The chapter of yoga propagation was complete and when one chapter closed, the next chapter opened.

Thus the World Yoga Convention also heralded the beginning of the second chapter of the Bihar School of Yoga.

The hallmark of this second chapter is a new vision of yoga not as a practice but as a *vidya*, a wisdom to be understood, imbibed and expressed in life. This understanding of the fundamental need for integral development was the vision of Swami Satyananda, which he imparted and taught through the concept of the *yoga chakra*, or the wheel of yoga.

The second chapter of the Bihar School of Yoga and the teachings which are being presented are not concerned with propagation of the practices of yoga. Isolated practices of yoga do not bring about the qualitative change and spiritual evolution intended and envisaged by the seers. The transcendence of the negative and restricting conditions and the real evolution and growth of the personality takes place only when the vidya of yoga is comprehended, absorbed and realized.

The profundity of yogic understanding must increase and the depths of yoga must be fathomed, if the vidya is to be realized and maintained for future generations. The experience and wisdom of accomplished yogis and spiritual scientists is recorded in the scriptural and classical texts detailing each anga of yoga. The second chapter teachings are a progressive effort to discern and elucidate the experiences and realizations of the ancient seers, within the blueprint of the yoga chakra.

For individual aspirants, the challenge of the second chapter is to deepen the understanding and experience of yoga. Practice is merely an introduction to yoga, which is limited by personal motivation and constraints. The yoga vidya dimension is accessed only when one moves from practice to sadhana and makes a sincere effort to experience the aims defined by the different angas of yoga. Until that sincerity awakens, the commitment to adhere to the system and the vidya of yoga is lacking. With sincerity, seriousness and commitment, each aspirant has to accept responsibility for their own development and betterment in life.

Ultimately, yoga is a lifestyle. It is not a practice. For, once the yogic principles are imbibed and become part of life, the attitudes, perceptions, interactions, the mind, actions and behaviours will improve. To meet the challenge of the second chapter, the expressive and the behavioural components of yoga, the antaranga and the bahiranga aspects, have to come together. When head, heart and hands unite, an ordinary moment can become divine. An ordinary life can become a divine life.

50 Years Marks
the Turning Point

The practices of yoga that you have adopted so far have not fulfilled the real needs in your life for you have never allowed them access into your life. The only way you can allow them access is by realizing that you need to connect with positivity and goodness. That has to be the state of mind of a spiritual sadhaka. That is the quality and nature of a spiritual sadhaka, to connect with positivity.

—*Swami Niranjanananda Saraswati*

In 1963 when Bihar School of Yoga was established in the remote town of Munger, Bihar, yoga was unheard of in the West. Even in India, yoga was a word associated with ascetics and renunciates in the Himalayas who practised austerities. Today, according to the statistical research available, millions of people across the globe practise something called 'yoga'. In America alone the number of people practising yoga has grown by over 50% in the last four years to over 36 million as of 2016. In common parlance the word yoga is used to refer to a series of asanas or even just physical practices which may or may not be derived from any classical traditional source.

This physical component of asana has taken the modern world of materialism by storm. Irrespective of culture, religion, social and economic circumstances, people are practising a form of physical exercise derived from yoga asana. The general understanding is that yoga is a set or series of physical practices much like gymnastics or Pilates, which can be done with any accessory or in any location. Paddle-yoga is asana performed on a paddleboard in the ocean. Aerial yoga is asana performed while hanging from the ceiling. Snoga is asana practised in the winter mountain landscape. Doga is yoga when you practise with your dog.

But this supermarket of yoga reflects what modern consumers want yoga to be. Yoga has become something that fits with individual interests, and reflects the latest fashion or fad. Choose your own brand, the list of fashionable varieties and combinations of different yogas available in the marketplace of health and fitness are almost endless. This proliferation of yoga styles is consumer driven diversity, and the popularity of different styles and brands is like anything else in the marketplace, largely determined by promotion, advertising and appeal. The growing interest in yoga is becoming a global fashion. A national survey done in America in 2016 showed yoga ranked among the five top growth industries with practitioners spending 16 billion dollars annually on equipment, clothing and accessories.

If a survey were to be conducted of what people thought about yoga, the majority of answers would include some sort of understanding of yoga as spiritual practice which led to self-realization, or if not spiritual realization at least some sort of qualitative improvement in life. But the question needs to be asked: If yoga is a spiritual practice which can bring about a positive change in life, is that positive change seen in the individuals who practise, and has that qualitative change manifested in society? Are people happier, are they experiencing greater contentment, peace and harmony in life because of the practice of yoga? Is any positive change being reflected in lifestyle and society?

Global news and information reports point to the opposite, a negative decline, not a positive change. The present era is defined by multiple and converging crises, a fact continually repeated by scientific experts and environmental, social, financial and political commentators. Many describe the major challenges we face as a planetary emergency, evidenced by worsening climate change and the ecological crisis in all its dimensions, as well as rising levels of extreme inequality and escalating conflicts over the world's dwindling natural resources. Despite gigantic leaps of science and technological advancement, we are unable to find solutions to the current situation, and the feeling of helplessness grows.

In the face of this unprecedented crisis, the society which developed, adopted and is now defined by technology, internet and social media, continues to promote the mirage of affluence, abundance and online availability. Across the globe digitalization of advertising is fuelling the fires of desire, greed, and ambition resulting in record levels of resource consumption. But something is missing. Peace, happiness and contentment have become so elusive, that entire sections of online sales and bookstores are dedicated to the quest to rediscover happiness in life. Happiness is now the subject of global concern, with annual reports being published to determine levels of happiness in different nations.

During the Golden Jubilee year of Bihar School of Yoga it was announced that during the fifty years from 1963 to 2013, the chapter of yoga propagation had been completed. Yoga has definitely spread from shore to shore and door to door, and a mandate has been fulfilled. Yet the global acceptance of yoga asana may owe more to the demand for physical health and attractiveness, than to any commitment to creating a positive change in personality and lifestyle. It is not that physical health and wellbeing are unimportant. Physical health is necessary and important, but a culture which promotes the physical and the material above all other aspects of life is encouraging imbalance.

If there was equal emphasis placed upon the development of emotional harmony and mental peace, the world would be a different place. The so-called spiritual values are often spoken of, but are these qualities reflected and expressed in the nature, thoughts, actions and behaviour of individuals who practise yoga? Mental health, emotional health and spiritual health are equally important, if not more important than a slim and flexible body. To lead a happy, optimistic and positive life, the body, mind, emotions and psyche all need to function properly and in harmony with each other.

The call for change
This imbalance, created by the emphasis on the material and physical aspects of life, is reflected in the choices which are made and the way in which society develops. There is no doubt of the urgency and need for change. Change is necessary for transformation, and transformation is necessary for spiritual evolution and transcendence. Change is the first step, and the three-fold change in attitude, approach and connection that is required of yoga aspirants was laid down by Swami Niranjanananda Saraswati during the Golden Jubilee of Bihar School of Yoga when he declared that sincerity, seriousness and commitment were needed to take the next step. This sincerity, seriousness and commitment needs to be understood firstly in relation to *yoga vidya*, the science of yoga, and secondly in relation to oneself as a yogic aspirant.

It is these two concepts that have formed the corner-stones for the second chapter of Bihar School of Yoga. Firstly, the connection to yoga, not just as a practice, but as a vidya. Secondly, the sincere commitment of the aspirant to identify and rectify the personal shortcomings which are the impediments to spiritual progress. These two cornerstones are interrelated and interdependent. Without the sincerity of the aspirant it will not be possible to connect with and imbibe the yoga vidya. Without the connection to the yoga vidya, there is no possibility to imbibe the teachings which enable one to observe and rectify one's own shortcomings. It is only through the connection to the yoga vidya that one can work towards a balanced integration and expression of the faculties of mind, emotions and body.

It is the mental transformation that will lead to happiness and peace. That is what you have to look for ultimately. Therefore, what you need is a practice, system or technique that can help you deal with your nature and mind.

—*Swami Niranjanananda Saraswati*

5

Part 1

The Need of the Hour

1

Yoga Vidya

Spirituality is a way to become a better person, a more human person.

—*Swami Niranjanananda Saraswati*

What we think we know about yoga is partial and limited. Most people come into contact with yoga through practice. The initial impetus to practise yoga is usually to achieve a certain aim, whether the management of lower back pain, weight loss, or to increase the flexibility of the body. If one comes to yoga with a physical aim or objective in mind, generally the connection remains defined by that need and is therefore limited. Once the desired outcome is attained, then the practice of yoga is discarded or continued depending upon the interest and enthusiasm for the practice. But yoga remains limited to being a practice, like golf, tennis or any other form of recreation.

The change begins when one is able to understand that there is more than the physical aspect of yoga; there is the possibility and the potential to access the mental, emotional and psychic dimensions of the human personality and transform these. This can only be achieved when yoga is understood and taken up as a sadhana. Understanding yoga to be a sadhana means one has to connect with the system, method and sequence that is prescribed in yoga, and follow that until the ultimate goal is attained. That ultimate goal is not a personal one, which the yoga aspirant defines for themselves, it is the final outcome which has been established and experienced by the spiritual *parampara*, tradition.

Through sadhana, one begins to connect with yoga as a vidya, not as a practice. *Vidya* is defined as knowledge, as wisdom, or as science. Yet more than this, vidya refers to the continuous transcendental stream of knowledge which exists in the purest state of truth. The aspect of vidya as wisdom or understanding, indicates the connection that the individual can make if the receptivity is there, if the sincerity and commitment is there. This connection is with vidya, not with personal expectations and preferences. In order to connect with vidya you need to be sincere about it, put aside personal expectations, preferences, likes and dislikes, and follow the system which has been laid down. For most people, the connection is formed at the intellectual level in the beginning, through a logical process of learning and study. However, when what is learnt intellectually is applied in life, then the connection to vidya can also become intuitive, receptive to the higher dimensions of existence.

Tantra and Vedanta
The origin of yoga is found in two separate traditions of spiritual thought and experience. One is tantra and the other is Vedanta. Vedanta speaks of the ultimate reality which is one, and sees the diversity of the world as an expansion of that one divine power. Tantra does not talk of the ultimate experience, but of the process to get there. Tantra and Vedanta can be viewed as two different traditions, but ultimately, when they are understood in the context of human experience, they are linked with each other.

Tantra begins with the relative form of knowledge, based on individual experience, and it is in the tantras that we find the practice-oriented aspects such as asana, pranayama, mudra and bandha, kriya and kundalini yoga and the practices of dhyana. Because tantra uses the relative processes of knowledge and experience, it does not emphasize the expressive and interactive aspect of life. Vedanta begins with the absolute and holds that everything is in essence divine. Therefore, Vedanta places great emphasis on lifestyle, the expressive and interactive aspect of the individual and how they relate with the universe.

It is like two rivers which merge to become one. Over thousands of years these two rivers have been flowing over rocks and mountains, valleys and plains. Once they are merged, the separate flows are intermingled and they cannot be separated. The current of the river created by the two flows is stronger and more powerful, and has a life of its own. This third river is yoga. Seen from this perspective it is clear that the reason there has been no progress or development in yoga is because of an imbalanced exposure and understanding. In order to connect with and imbibe a vidya, you cannot pick and choose what to learn, because what has been selected is partial, incomplete, and based on personal preference. Until the proper system of learning is followed, there will not be any progress and the huge gap in understanding will remain.

This is the current situation. What has been grasped of yoga is the physical component of asana derived from the tantras, according to individual interest and desires. The physical component is highlighted and by doing so individualism and self-oriented perception accentuated. What has been completely ignored is the lifestyle component derived from Vedanta, which emphasizes not the separate individual but the interconnectedness of life, and how to think, feel, act and interact in the world. The development of selflessness, the ability to connect with all of life and express that connection in generosity, understanding, love, compassion is missing. This lopsided development is because only a tiny part of the yoga vidya has been selected, and the rest has been ignored.

11

What is the relevance of yoga today? The moment you manage the intellect, emotions and actions, you give evolution a chance in your lives.

—*Swami Niranjanananda Saraswati*

Paramapara

Spiritual *paramparas* or traditions provide the solution to this problem. The concept of a spiritual parampara evolved to preserve and propagate the vidya. Paramparas are formed by individuals, the spiritual scientists who utilized their lives as laboratories in order to perfect different aspects of experience, and reach the apex of understanding and revelation. The level of expertise attained in a particular realm of vidya, develops into a body of knowledge, methodology, philosophy and practice. The luminaries of traditions are the visionaries who are endowed with the ability and the experience to further enhance and develop the knowledge.

Paramparas are there to help spiritual aspirants, by defining the system of what should be learnt, how it should be learnt and when it should be learnt. The spiritual parampara defines the process, stages and development of learning. Those who become part of the tradition do so by following that system, faithfully, without trying to adjust it to their own personal likes and dislikes. If that effort is sincere, then a connection develops with the essence of the vidya, which permeates and transforms the entire personality. If that connection is not sincere, if it is partial, half-hearted or inadequate, then nothing happens. No change, no growth, no evolution, no transformation in life.

In order to make a positive contribution to society in times of need, different teachings are revealed by the luminaries of spiritual traditions at different times. It is like the different terrain through which the river of yoga vidya flows over thousands of years. Sometimes the terrain is mountainous and full of rocks, sometimes narrow and twisting through valleys and fiords, at other times the terrain is so unsuitable that the river has to go underground and is hidden from sight. It all depends on the social conditions of the time. What is relevant, appropriate and necessary becomes the spiritual teaching of the age.

The Buddha taught and propagated the teaching of *ahimsa*, because the principle of non-violence was essential to society at that time. In the 1900s witnessing the violence of two world wars and the devastation and suffering which followed, Swami Sivananda felt compelled to disseminate his spiritual teachings to the world. His message was simple, life is divine and this divinity can be experienced. To experience divinity, purify and spiritualize the mind, open the heart, connect with life and express this positive connection in action. His message shone like a beacon in the darkness and inspired countless people to tread the path of spirituality and yoga.

Swami Sivananda began investigating the possibilities of yoga as a science which could be utilized for the upliftment of humanity. This was a visionary idea and perspective, because at that time yoga was practised by sannyasins and renunciates who had severed their ties with society and pursued a different lifestyle, based on principles designed to encourage spiritual evolution. Swami Sivananda called his yoga integral yoga, or the yoga of synthesis. His philosophy was Vedanta, the divinity of the universe, the unity of all creation with the absolute, all-pervading Brahman. For Swami Sivananda, his integral yoga was the means to achieve this realization. Warning against imbalanced development, Swami Sivananda's teachings were based on a combination of the different branches of yoga, as well as practical Vedanta.

The Need of the Hour

When man gets entangled in selfishness, greed, lust, passion, he naturally forgets all about spiritual life. He always thinks of his body, family and children. He constantly attends to his food, drink, comforts and conveniences. He is drowning in the ocean of *samsara* or the world. Materialism and scepticism reign supreme. He gets irritated by little things and begins to fight. There is restlessness, misery, panic and chaos everywhere. Now the whole world seems to be in the grip of materialism. The invention of new kings of bombs causes terror everywhere. People have lost faith in holy scriptures and the teachings of the saints and sages.

The stirring events since the advent of the twentieth century did not fail to have their effect on all spiritual-minded people, sannyasins, saints. The horrors of world wars moved them greatly. The fateful epidemic and the worldwide depression that followed it, touched their compassionate hearts. They saw that the sufferings of mankind were mostly brought on by his own deeds. To awaken man to his errors and follies and to make him mend his ways so that he may enthusiastically utilize his life for attaining worthier ends was felt to be the urgent need of the age.

Millions were eagerly looking for such guidance. This silent prayer was heard and I saw the birth of the Divine Life Mission with its task of rescuing man from the forces of bestiality and brutality and divinizing life upon this planet. Just at this critical juncture I started the Divine Life Society. Although the central basis is Vedanta, it is necessary for one to practise karma yoga for purity of mind and health, hatha yoga to keep up good health and strength, purify the prana and strengthen the mind, raja yoga to destroy the sankalpas and induce concentration in meditation, and jnana yoga to remove the veil of ignorance and ultimately rest in one's own self or *satchidananda swarupa*.

—*Swami Sivananda Saraswati*

15

This vision of the role that yoga would play in modern society propelled an evolution in the tradition of sannyasa. Swami Sivananda saw yoga as a science which would improve the quality of life for each individual, and encourage harmony and virtue in society. Therefore, the best teachers of yoga would be those who had a spiritual identity and lifestyle based on the principles of Vedanta and could discern the essence of the yoga vidya. The disciples of Swami Sivananda although initiated in sannyasa, were given the mission and mandate of yoga propagation, and their training was in the vidya of yoga. The mandate of yoga propagation naturally brought forth a new development in sannyasa. Sannyasins were no longer isolated from the mainstream and engaged in sadhana, but went forth, travelled and lived within society.

Swami Sivananda's disciples Swami Satyananda, Swami Venkateshananda, Swami Satchidananda, Swami Sahajananda and Swami Vishnudevananda are notable examples of this first wave of sannyasins who interacted with society in order to propagate the mandate of yoga given by their guru. Their focus was the integration of the faculties of head, heart and hands, and this encouraged the incorporation of yoga into daily life, in the hope that it would transform people's lifestyle.

Swami Satyananda established Bihar School of Yoga as a yoga school, but also as an ashram. From inception, Bihar School of Yoga was not just a campus where students could come to learn yoga, it was also a spiritual centre where sincere aspirants could dedicate themselves to the parampara and live yoga. The teachings given to these two groups of people were different, yet the necessity of integral yoga was always emphasized. Swami Satyananda taught hatha yoga, raja yoga and kriya yoga in a sequential and systematic progression through the *bahiranga* or external aspect of yoga. Side by side the *antaranga* or internal aspect was imbibed and expressed through karma yoga, bhakti yoga and jnana yoga by aspirants who made the effort to live the yogic lifestyle of the ashram.

The same adherence to integral sadhana and connection to vidya is seen in the teachings of Swami Niranjanananda. Focusing on the need to deepen the experience of yoga, his teachings show the importance of connecting with vidya, to express wisdom in life. As a yoga aspirant, seriousness means making the connection with yoga as a vidya, not as a fashion or fad to indulge the whims of today and the fantasy of tomorrow. Sincerity means being honest and taking responsibility for individual shortcomings which are obstructing the connection with vidya and the application of the teachings in life. Commitment means the determination to improve, enhance and express the positive qualities in life.

If you say you are a practitioner of yoga, then you have to look at the whole picture of yoga and your involvement in it. This is where your own sincerity, seriousness and commitment comes into play.

—*Swami Niranjanananda Saraswati*

2

The Six Conditions

What greater undertaking lies before you than purifying
your life of all enmity, impurity, hatred, passion, and
filling it with love, goodness, peace and purity?

—*Swami Sivananda Saraswati*

The yoga vidya is accessible through the spiritual parampara,
through the teachings, wisdom, philosophy and experience
of spiritual luminaries, sages, rishis and munis of ancient as
well as contemporary times. In different ways, at different
times the teachings of yoga vidya which are revealed for
the benefit of society all proclaim that bliss, peace and
harmony are the birthright of humankind. But, despite so
many opportunities, we fail to experience the truth of these
teachings or imbibe them in our lives.

This is not a new phenomenon, Swami Sivananada
wrote about this in the 1930s, when he explained that while
listening to his satsangs the audience motivated more by
vanity than anything else, would pretend to understand and
receive the flow of wisdom nodding their heads, yet they
seldom practised and were unable to apply to the teachings
in daily life.

If the blazing blue sky were to pour down torrents of light on an assembly of blind men, they would feel the heat but see no light. Similarly, when I provide life-giving wisdom through the channels of a discourse or speech or writing, you may be stirred to involuntary thrills at the graceful succession of rhythmic sentences or, moved by vanity, pretend to understand and receive the flow of wisdom nodding your heads as if in complete understanding. If a few of you penetrate into the substance of the speech or the writing and grasp the truth of it, they seldom practise; and even if a few among you translate the wisdom into action or apply it to your daily lives, you are insincere, or rather forced to be insincere by the subtle desires, secret schemes and screened hopes lodged in the innermost recess of your hearts.

—*Swami Sivananda Saraswati*

This incapacity to observe, study and remove the obstacles which impede spiritual progress is what Swami Sivananda referred to as 'the great tragedy'. It is the urgency of effort needed to address this great tragedy which has compelled the attention of Swami Niranjanananda following the Golden Jubilee of Bihar School of Yoga, and has inspired the teachings of the second chapter. There are two cornerstones for the second chapter of yoga. One is the connection with the yoga vidya, which can only happen if we sincerely follow the system of yoga which has been laid down. The other is the seriousness, sincerity and commitment which allows us to acknowledge and make the effort to overcome the obstacles, the weakness, limitations, and shortcomings which prevent us from imbibing the teachings of yoga in life.

These obstacles lie in the mind. The mind controls and directs the actions and behaviour in life. Life is created by the mind, and the relationship one has with the world is determined by the mind. A happy mind will determine happy interactions and a happy life. A negative, critical and hostile mind will create an unhappy, lonely and isolated life. According to yoga and spiritual traditions, six traits are embedded in the human mind and expressed in the personality. In different combinations and permutations these six help to create the nature, mindset, personality, habits, traits and character. These personality traits are known as the six enemies, or *shat-ripu*, active obstacles to spiritual progress. Alternatively, they are spoken of as the six conditions or associates, because although detrimental these six are constant companions to the mind, and like conditions who constantly give advice and suggestion, are able to influence the personality.

These six are the conditions of mind. They create the mental conditioning that entangle the mind in the material dimension of experience and through selfishness constrict the development of the personality. The six conditions are:

1. *Kama*, meaning the desire and passion which exists and is inherent in every life form.
2. *Krodha*, representing all manifestations of anger and the aggressive drive in life.
3. *Lobha*, or greed which is the self-centred condition of covetousness that emphasizes personal needs and expresses in accumulation, hoarding and selfishness.
4. *Moha* refers to the state of mind which is deluded and infatuated.
5. *Mada* is the state of pride, arrogance, and all other forms of the self-assertive identity.
6. *Matsarya* is the condition of envy and jealousy.

These six traits are the architects of human nature, they design, create and construct the personality. It is very difficult to counteract their influence, input and projections.

Lead an ideal life of peace. Ruthlessly kill suspicion, prejudice of all sorts, envy, selfishness, greed for power and possessions. Lead a simple life. Practise daily meditation and establish peace in your own heart. Then radiate it to your neighbours and all who come in contact with you. Disseminate it far and wide.

—*Swami Sivananda Saraswati*

Everything which is experienced is perceived and categorized by the mind into experiences which are good or bad. This is the first and most basic reaction which arises in the mind in response to any sensory or non-sensory input. In yogic terminology this is referred to as the categorization of *raga* or like and *dwesha* or dislike. In the *Yoga Sutras*, Patanjali describes raga as *sukha anusayi ragah* (2:7) which means that raga is the liking which accompanies pleasure. The desire to unite with something, to come closer to something or someone is raga. Dwesha on the other hand is *duhkha anusayi dvesah* (2:6), translated as the repulsion accompanying pain. The desire to avoid, repel and get away from something or someone is dwesha. From this perspective, both raga and dwesha are actually desires: the desire to get closer to something pleasurable and the desire to get away from something that is painful.

In raga there is a state of expansion in the mind and personality. A feeling of warmth and openness to life develops. The opposite is experienced in the state of dwesha. In dwesha there is aversion, trying to avoid the situation, distance and separate oneself from the experience. A contraction takes place in the mind and the personality feels cold and closed. Neither of these qualities of raga and dwesha exist in objects themselves, but they exist in the senses to bring forth the experience of joy or grief, pleasure or pain. Therefore, the senses have to be properly managed. If the senses are indulged and not restrained, they become the cause of suffering and an obstacle to mental peace and happiness. In the *Bhagavad Gita* Krishna explains this saying (3:34):

इन्द्रियस्येन्द्रियस्यार्थे रागद्वेषौ व्यवस्थितौ ।
तयोर्न वशमागच्छेत्तो ह्यस्य परिपन्थिनौ ॥

Indriyasyendriyasyaarthe raagadweshau vyavasthitau;
Tayor na vasham aagacchet tau hyasya paripanthinau.

Attachment and aversion for the objects of the senses abide in the senses; let none come under their sway, for they are obstacles.

Raga and dwesha can be understood as two sides of the one experience. They are not separate. The extent to which one experiences raga or attachment for an object is exactly the same extent to which one will experience dwesha or revulsion for another. It is like the swinging of a pendulum. During the mental reaction of raga, as one tries to get closer to attain the object of desire, the pendulum of the mind arcs widely to the right. In the experience of dwesha, as one experiences revulsion and tries to distance oneself, the pendulum of the mind swings to the left in exactly the same trajectory. Raga and dwesha are a twofold experience of a mental reaction which causes suffering and disturbs the peace of mind. These two responses condition the mind to swing from one to the other, and thereby the peaceful state of harmony which rests in the middle is never attained. The swing of raga and dwesha keeps one identified with the external world and does not allow the mind to connect with the inner nature.

As long as the pendulum of raga and dwesha dominates the mind, the focus is self-centric and limited to 'me and mine'. This self-centred focus which highlights 'me' as a separate entity from the world, is known as *dvaita bhava*, or the feeling of duality. It is this dvaita bhava which the teachings of Vedanta seek to transcend. Vedanta proclaims *advaita bhava*, the experience of non-duality or spiritual oneness. Advaita bhava is not simply a metaphysical idea or moral principle, it is the deepest consciousness which lies within every being as a reality to be experienced. In different manifest forms this essence animates the entire existence, it illumines every being and connects all the individual forms of life by an invisible thread into an eternal universal existence of truth, consciousness and bliss, *satchidananda*. The six conditions are the obstacles to experiencing the expansion of consciousness and awareness which culminates in advaita bhava. If there was no feeling of separateness or duality, no concept of me as a separate and isolated ego, the six conditions would have no relevance. However, when dvaita bhava predominates, the six conditions arise as reactions to the experiences of raga or dwesha.

> Ultimately, to deepen the yogic experience one has to alter the natural or conditioned behaviour pattern. This pertains to the six friends kama, krodha, lobha, moha, mada, matsarya – passion, aggression, greed, infatuation, arrogance, envy – the six colours of the mind. Just as when light passes through a prism you see a range of colours, when the light of any information passes through the mind it is seen in relation to one of these colours. An idea comes and it becomes your kama, another becomes your krodha, your lobha, your moha. Anything that comes to the mind from outside is separated into one of these colours of mental expression and that is what is perceived.
>
> —*Swami Niranjanananda Saraswati*

The three conditions which arise from the reaction of raga are kama, lobha and moha. They are all expressions of raga in which the focus and orientation of the mind is towards attaining something pleasant for oneself. Kama which encompasses all forms and manifestations of desire is an obvious expression of raga. The desire is to attain for oneself. Lobha is greed, the desire for excess that creates imbalance in life. Moha is also an extension of raga, because in the state of moha one is deluded and infatuated, perceiving external circumstances and situations according to one's individual idiosyncrasies, likes and dislikes. Moha occurs when the self-centric perception takes over completely, and the individual perceives themselves to be the centre of the universe. All objectivity is lost. Everything that is experienced, all the interactions, circumstances and events are interpreted subjectively and manipulated by the moha fuelled intellect to become a self-fulfilling prophecy.

The remaining three conditions born from the reaction of dwesha are krodha, matsyarya and mada. Krodha is the expression of anger which comes up in relation to a situation, person, or experience which one does not like. The entire spectrum of the krodha response ranges from violence, hostility, aggression, to negativity, criticism and impatience. Matsarya is the reaction of jealousy or envy which arises in relation to a person one dislikes. Because of the dwesha, because of the dislike, enmity or hatred experienced in relation to a particular person, there is always a reaction of jealousy or envy when the happiness or good fortune of that person is perceived. Mada which refers to the state of arrogance, pride and the self-assertive identity is also a reaction in which the ego attempts to project itself in order to dominate or feel in control of a situation or person. The response of mada arises because there is something in that situation or individual which threatens or creates a feeling of insecurity, and to overcome and compensate for this the arrogant and proud nature comes to the forefront.

The key to managing these negative qualities lies in the connection with yoga vidya and an integral approach to sadhana. Hatha yoga practices assist in the detoxification and purification of the body, brain, senses and nervous system. Jnana yoga techniques develop the ability to observe, analyze and correct one's thoughts, attitudes and expressions in life. The pratyahara teachings of raja yoga provide methods to manage the senses and reduce the influence of sensorial inputs in the mind. Side by side the techniques of yama and niyama need to be used, to help curb and restrain the negative activity of the mind and provide positive inputs. Sourced in the teachings of Vedanta, yama and niyama are eternal principles which if practised correctly connect one with the positive expressions of head, heart and hands.

Peace is not in the heart of the carnal man. Peace is not in the hearts of ministers, advocates, businessmen, dictators, kings and emperors. Peace is in the hearts of yogis, sages, saints and spiritual men. It is in the heart of a desireless man, who has controlled his senses and the mind. Greed, lust, jealousy, envy, anger, pride, and egoism are the enemies of peace. Slay these enemies by the sword of dispassion, discrimination, and non-attachment. You will enjoy perpetual peace.

—*Swami Sivananda Saraswati*

3

Lifestyle Yama and Niyama

Spiritual thought is developing positive qualities in life and overcoming negativities.

—*Swami Niranjanananda Saraswati*

What are the yamas and niyamas? Awareness and adherence to certain qualities and ideas which can uplift the human mind, emotions, character, psyche and personality. You become and are recognized as being a good person. If you develop the quality of *ahimsa*, non-violence, you will emanate compassion. If you develop the quality of *satya*, truthfulness, you will emanate love. If you imbibe the quality of *aparigraha*, non-possessiveness, you will express simplicity and innocence. Each yama and each niyama will highlight a character of the human personality. When that character is highlighted then it becomes part of your expression, understanding, actions, behaviour, attitude and life. Therefore, yoga is not only techniques, it is also a lifestyle, known as the yogic lifestyle.

Alongside the need for seriousness, sincerity and commitment, we need to connect and provide positive inputs to the mind. Positive mental input supports the development of faith, conviction and helps to create a balanced mind. It is not possible to confront and manage the limiting and negative aspects of mind without mental balance and a connection to positivity. Methods to create and maintain positive qualities of mind are given in the second chapter teachings of Bihar School of Yoga.

> The yogic knowledge which you apply in your life is confined to some hatha yoga, asana, pranayama, shatkarma and maybe a little bit of raja yoga. It is a general trait. The big chunk of knowledge missing from life is contained in the yamas and niyamas. It is the application of yamas and niyamas that will allow you to experience the wholeness and completeness of yoga.
>
> —*Swami Niranjanananda Saraswati*

The first aspect involves connecting with positive qualities, attitudes and expressions of mind. In yoga and Vedanta, these qualities and expressions are known as yama and niyama. *Yama* is a positive, condition or experience of mind that is sattwic. *Niyama* is the expression of that positive quality in daily life. Yama and niyama are techniques of sadhana that date back to the vedic period, an era socially, philosophically and spiritually different from the society of today. Vedic culture and society reflected a different way of thinking, acting and living that emerged through collective effort and dedication to developing a spiritual understanding and experience of life.

The importance of developing positive qualities of personality as the foundation for spiritual experience was reflected in the systems of education that included both material and spiritual education, and sought to find a balance and harmony between the two. This understanding was the basis for lifestyle and people lived according to the principles of dharma, making the effort to develop, enhance and express the spiritual principles in daily life. Yamas and niyamas evolved from this environment of dharma, and over time were understood as important spiritual sadhanas.

People think of yamas and niyamas as ethical and moral teachings. That is incorrect. They are an expression, a behaviour, and a conditioning of the mind. In moments of strife, you want to discover peace. So why not also try to discover love, compassion, sympathy, understanding and joy?

—*Swami Niranjanan-ananda Saraswati*

Today yama and niyama are almost completely overlooked and if at all understood, their utility is relegated to a code of conduct or discipline. This is an incorrect understanding. Yama and niyama are the natural outcome of an integral yoga sadhana and a yogic lifestyle. When the sadhana is appropriate and the lifestyle is regulated, restrained, harmonious and balanced, the positive qualities of yama and niyama manifest spontaneously. It is like a mango tree, when the environmental conditions are conducive, the tree naturally yields sweet, juicy, delicious fruit that can be enjoyed by all. In the same way, the inner spiritual nature needs the correct inputs and conditions in order to flourish and bear fruit in the form of the positive qualities of life.

Just as soap cleanses the physical body, so the practice of yama cleanses the mind of its impurities.

—*Swami Sivananda Saraswati*

Each branch of yoga has its own set of yamas and niyamas according to the aim and purpose of that yoga. Apart from these, Swami Niranjananananda has explained a set of yamas and niyamas drawn from the yogic scriptures that create and support a yogic lifestyle. Lifestyle plays a crucial role in transformation. It is through lifestyle, discipline and routine that positive changes in thinking patterns, attitudes, behaviour and habits are possible, and these changes ultimately transform the personality. The best place to understand, imbibe and experience this lifestyle component of yoga is in an ashram. In the same way that vedic society

28

was totally different from the material world of today, the ashram environment is completely different from worldly life. Formed according to principles, disciplines and attitudes that promote spiritual progress and transformation, the ashram environment is sattwic.

> Yama and niyama relate to lifestyle, for they represent the emergence of a better, positive conditioning. They always connect you with a positive dimension of your nature and are an antidote to the negative. You think that asana and pranayama, the physical aspects of yoga, as the catalysts to lead you to a different state of mind. It is not going to happen. You think of meditation and mantra as the catalysts to develop a better mind. It will not happen. Until and unless you think of incorporating little changes in your life, fine-tuning your life, you will not live the change. This fine-tuning can be done though yama and niyama.

> —*Swami Niranjanananda Saraswati*

Lifestyle combined with yama and niyama provide the catalyst for the development of a better mind. Evolution and transformation of mind takes place when selfishness lessens and a selfless connection with one's environment develops.

The six lifestyle yamas
1. **Manahprasad**: Happiness without an external cause. Happiness is your true nature – this has to be realized by connecting with the positive side of your personality and the beauty of life. No matter what circumstances you find yourself in, look within and smile at yourself and the situation at hand. This will change your perspective. Manahprasad is an antidote to kama.

2. **Kshama**: Forgiveness. The ability to let go of feelings of resentment, anger or hurt by clearing out the negativity through forgiveness and returning to a state of happiness and balance. Kshama is an antidote to krodha and mada.

29

3. **Danti**: Mental restraint. The ability to empty the mind of negativity and to live with contentment and inner discipline. Nothing should build up in the mind to the point where it results in an outward explosion. Danti is an antidote to krodha, kama and lobha.

4. **Adweshta**: To be without envy, hatred, separation and the feeling of division. Adweshta means to have equal vision, without differentiation. Adweshta is an antidote to matsyara and krodha.

5. **Bhava shuddhi**: Purity of intention. Bhava shuddhi is expressed though *sadvichara*, *sadvyavahara*, *satkarma*, right thinking, right behaviour and right action. Bhava shuddhi is an antidote to krodha, lobha, moha and matsarya.

6. **Shantata**: Serenity and balance. To maintain a balanced state in all circumstances, without distraction or dissipation. Shantata is experienced as inner equipoise and peace. It is an antidote to krodha, mada and matsarya.

> Man is the master of his own destiny. He sows an action and reaps a habit; sows a habit and reaps a character; sows a character and reaps a destiny.
>
> —*Swami Sivananda Saraswati*

The six lifestyle niyamas

1. **Japa**: Repetition of mantra. Japa disconnects you from the activities of the senses and allows the mind to turn inward to discover inner happiness and contentment. Japa is paired with manahprasad and is an antidote to kama.

2. **Namaskara**: Salutations toward another person. Namaskara connects you with humility and allows you to express goodwill, kindness and openness. Namaskara is paired with kshama and is an antidote to krodha.

3. **Indriya nigraha**: Management and withdrawal from sensorial dissipation. In indriya nigraha you cultivate disciplined and appropriate use of the senses. Indriya nigraha is paired with danti and is an antidote to krodha, kama and lobha.

4. **Maitri**: Friendliness and goodwill to all. Maitri begins with self-acceptance and then extends to all in the spirit of goodwill and understanding. Paired with adweshta maitri is an antidote to krodha and matsarya.

5. **Titiksha**: Patience and endurance. Titiksha develops stability and contentment. It complements bhava shuddhi and is an antidote to krodha, lobha, moha and matsarya.

6. **Niyamitata**: Regularity. Expressed through lifestyle, niyamitata represents simplicity, discipline, moderation and balance. It complements shantata and is an antidote to krodha, mada and matsarya.

Two sets of lifestyle yama and niyama techniques have been prescribed by Swami Niranjanananda for the management of krodha. Firstly the yama of danti and the niyama of indriya nigraha, and secondly the yama of shantata and the niyama of niyamitata. Indriya nigraha can be understood as sensorial restraint, and danti as mental restraint. When there is imbalance, restraint is needed to again bring about a state of balance and harmony. At the personal level, krodha creates an imbalance in body, mind and emotions. This causes suffering, insecurity and instability at the individual and social levels. The Sanskrit word nigraha is comprised of the word 'graha' which comes from *grahan* meaning to hold or receive, and the prefix *ni* which indicates negation. Indriya nigraha is not receiving, not holding on to, withdrawing and letting go of the sensorial input and the associated mental responses. Danti means not getting caught up in the mental experience of krodha, and practice of danti cultivates the ability to restrain and withdraw the influence of the vritti upon the mind.

The practice of indriya nigraha naturally and spontaneously leads one to niyamitata. When you realize the negative impact of unrestrained and imbalanced sensorial activity on the body, mind and emotions, the focus of change naturally turns to lifestyle. Small adjustments are made, and these are regularly applied and experienced in daily life. This

31

is niyamitata, the process of regulation and fine-tuning of lifestyle that returns balance to life. From a balanced lifestyle comes the experience of shantata, serenity and calm.

Vedanta speaks of reality as one essence, permeating every other experience. It is 'that' which connects all of life. All forms of life exist because of that essence. It is the same essential higher consciousness, which in its role as *maya*, the restrictive, binding force, has diverted the awareness of the mind into the senses. When the senses and the mind interact with each other, they produce different experiences. If the mind is purified and the senses are under control, the experiences will be positive. If the senses are unruly and krodha influences the mind, experiences will be limited, restricted and selfish. Through the influence of krodha, the connection with the higher consciousness is lost in the pursuit of personal vindication and domination.

To connect with that transcendental experience once more, we have to work progressively to purify, manage and restrain the different negative influences. This happens through the practice and expression of yama and niyama.

Just as there are doors in a bungalow between the outer and inner rooms, so also there are doors between the lower and higher minds. When the mind is purified by the practice of karma yoga, tapas, right conduct or the practice of yama, niyama, japa, meditation, etc., the doors between the lower and the higher mind are opened. Discrimination between the real and the unreal dawns. The eye of intuition is opened. The practitioner gets inspiration, revelation and higher Divine Knowledge.

—*Swami Sivananda Saraswati*

Part 2

What is Anger?

4

Identifying Krodha

Anger is only a modification or form of desire. Anger is desire itself.

—*Swami Sivananda Saraswati*

Krodha is usually translated to mean anger, but from the yogic perspective this is incomplete. Krodha is a *vritti*, a particular frequency of mental energy that completely alters the pattern of mental behaviour and thoughts. Vrittis are described as being circular in form, which means they can expand infinitely and contract without losing their shape, form or strength. When this field of influence is dominant in the mind, krodha creates its own pattern of thought, experience and expression. This manifests in a multitude of ways, from frowning, impatience, irritation, frustration, criticism, from gossip to indignation, hostility, aggression, rage, fury and violence.

Anger is just one expression of krodha: the aggressive and negative emotional reaction to a perceived provocation or threat. This instinctive response mechanism for protection and preservation is evident in both animals and humans. Dogs growl, bark and bare their teeth in response to an unfamiliar person or perceived threat to their territory. A female dog will react with ferocious anger to protect her puppies. People also react in anger when they perceive something or someone to be threatening, offensive or insulting. An angry person will identify a specific event, interaction or person as the cause of their anger. The reaction of anger is always projected onto an external cause, but in reality the cause of anger is krodha, the vritti that manifests in the mind.

Krodha arises from raga and dwesha, the mental experience of attachment and aversion. *Raga* is the desire to possess or attach to something pleasurable and *dwesha* is the desire to be free of something or someone unpleasant. From this perspective, raga and dwesha are the opposite ends of the same experience. That experience is desire. This is why although they seem and feel to be opposite, their effect upon the mind is the same. In attachment, the mind spontaneously and naturally gravitates towards the object of attachment. A mother naturally thinks of her children, and the mental connection that binds them is love. With dwesha, two enemies cannot stop thinking about one another and their minds fixate on the object of dislike, unable to break the connection of hate and negativity.

It is the same with kama and krodha, the first evolutes of raga and dwesha. Kama is desire and krodha is the negative aspect of desire. Kama is desire for something pleasurable and krodha is the desire to be free from something unpleasant. The impetus towards violence, vengeance and retaliation, the need to dominate and bully, these are all negative desires embedded in the different expressions of krodha. Krodha also creates and sustains a connection between the individual and the other person or the object of displeasure. The vritti strengthens that connection through repetition of negativity. Every expression of hostility, resentment and frustration strengthens the bond of krodha existing between two people.

Physiological experience
Before krodha is experienced in any part of the body, it has to affect the brain first. The brain is the internal alarm system that processes emotional stress. It signals to the rest of the body when we are happy, sad, angry, or in pain. When

the brain senses threat or harm, millions of nerve fibres within the brain release chemicals throughout the body to every organ. The first reaction happens inside two almond-shaped structures called the amygdala which is part of the limbic system of the brain. The amygdala is responsible for security and safety and its job is to perceive and identify threats in the environment and send warnings. This alarm system is so efficient that it can send messages before the cortex, the part of the brain responsible for thought and judgment, is able to check on the reasonableness of the reaction. In other words, the brain is hardwired to influence action before the consequences of actions can be thought about.

When this alarm system within the brain identifies a threat, it releases neurotransmitter chemicals known as catecholamins causing a burst of energy lasting up to several minutes. This burst of energy is the signal for immediate protective action, which then triggers a heightened reaction in other parts of the body. The stress hormones, adrenaline and noradrenaline are released. They help the body control the heart rate and blood pressure. Adrenaline creates a state of heightened awareness and responsiveness. Adrenaline causes glucose to gush through the blood stream and muscles giving the ability to respond faster, run faster, and make quicker decisions. The body's muscles tense up. Everything goes on alert.

The result is increased heart rate, heightened arterial tension and blood pressure. Testosterone production in-creases, the rib cage tenses, the rate of breathing increases and becomes irregular. The heart goes from pumping four litres per minute to pumping twenty litres per minute. More blood flows to the limbs and extremities in preparation for the anticipated physical action. The nostrils flare. The jaw tenses. The brow muscles move inward and downward, fixing a hard stare on the target. The body is mobilized for immediate action. This fight or flight reaction primes the body to either attack or run away.

Anger is a violent reaction. It may be the outcome of any issue, major or minor. In the state of anger, which has clouded your understanding, perception and logic, which has altered your body chemistry so that you are sweating and trembling, your face is flushed, your blood pressure is high and your breathing is shallow, you have subjected yourself to a violent expression of an emotion. That emotion is a reaction.

—*Swami Niranjanananda Saraswati*

It is the job of the prefrontal cortex of the brain to restrain and keep emotions in proportion. The prefrontal cortex is located just behind the forehead and it is the part of the brain where conscious control and decision-making processes occur. The ability to negotiate oneself out of a vritti, or a dominant pattern of thought, emotion, reaction and behaviour, is due to the activity of the prefrontal cortex. If the amygdala handles emotion, the prefrontal cortex handles judgment. When the sensory input is at a low to moderate stress level, the prefrontal cortex is able to intervene and calm the amygdala down.

This delays the release of hormones and the corresponding physiological changes. It allows time for the pros and cons of the intended behaviour to be considered. However, when the tolerance threshold is lower, or the stimulus is extreme, the activation of the amygdala can shut off the prefrontal cortex function. This shut down of the prefrontal cortex is called the amygdala hijack, when the conscious part of the brain automatically is turned off. The hijack is a purely instinctive response to the environment during which the instinctive brain is in control. The energy sent to the prefrontal cortex is greatly reduced and more than 75% of conscious reasoning is lost.

The whole nervous system is shattered by an outburst of anger. The eyes become red, the body quivers, the legs and hands tremble. No one can check an angry man. He gets enormous strength for the time being and gets a collapse after sometime on account of reaction.

—*Swami Sivananda Saraswati*

As well as the preparation phase during which physical and pranic resources are mobilized for a fight, krodha also has a wind-down phase. When the target or the circumstantial trigger is no longer immediately present, the physiological reaction begins to wind down. This takes time. The adrenaline caused arousal can last for hours or days. While adrenaline is in the system, the tolerance threshold is drastically lowered, making it much easier and more likely for krodha to take over the entire physical and mental behaviour. During the cool-down period, people are more likely to react aggressively in response to minor issues that normally would not evoke any reaction.

> Various poisons are thrown into the blood when one is angry. Fiery dark arrows shoot out from the astral body. These can be seen clearly by the clairvoyant eye. In the light of modern psychology, all diseases take their origin in anger. Rheumatism, heart-disease, nervous disease are all due to anger. It takes some months for the restoration of normal equilibrium in the nervous system.

—*Swami Sivananda Saraswati*

Impact upon health

Experiencing anger and aggressive reactionary behaviour can cause an average blood pressure of 120 over 80 to jump to 220 over 130 or higher. The body releases chemicals that clot the blood. These blood clots can create serious health problems and travel up the blood vessels to the brain or heart causing a stroke or heart attack. The risk of a heart attack is 8.5 times higher in the two hours after an outburst of extreme anger. The risk of a stroke is 3 times higher. In krodha the muscles that are needed to fight or flee become tense and uptight. This can lead to tension headaches, migraines, insomnia, body ache and fatigue.

Habitual krodha creates a chemical imbalance in the body and brain. Cortisol, the stress hormone, is released and can also cause an imbalance in blood sugar, suppress thyroid function and decrease bone density. The hormonal imbalance caused by excess of cortisol also influences the body's immune system. Chronically angry people suffer more frequently from colds, flus, sore throats, cough, infections, asthma, skin disease flare-ups and arthritis.

> The root-cause for diseases is selfishness. The root-cause is anger. The root-cause is malice. When you are angry, impurities are thrown in the blood. Hatred bacilli, malice bacilli, jealousy bacilli enter your system and produce diseases.
>
> —*Swami Sivananda Saraswati*

Krodha also negatively influences the nervous system. People who experience and have high levels of aggression and hostility show weaker parasympathetic nervous system responses. This imbalance affects the ability to relax and release the effects of stressful situations and circumstances. The hormone acetylcholine released by the parasympathetic nervous system is one of the ways that the body can counteract the arousal of the emotions of anger. Acetylcholine neutralizes the stress hormones and helps the body to relax and calm down. When krodha becomes part of the habitual repetitive behaviour, the ability of the nervous system to realign and balance the body is lost.

> When a thought of anger comes into your mind, what do you do? You just let yourself go; you fall into it; you do not even try to clean it out of the mind. That is why you are suffering from anxiety, fear, depression, dejection and anger. These thoughts are hitting your mind, infecting your mind just like a virus causes havoc

in your body. But a thought is more dangerous, powerful and effective than an ordinary physical virus. When a virus enters your body, it can be treated by certain drugs and medicines. But when a thought enters, when fear strikes, when passions and anxiety get into your mind, do you know what far-reaching effects it is going to have? Therefore, when we talk about health, we must definitely understand that we lack proper knowledge about the health of the mind, the health of the inner being.

—*Swami Satyananda Saraswati*

Neurological experience of krodha

According to neuroplasticity, practice leads to perfection. Venting and expressing krodha doesn't mean you have alleviated or curbed the reaction. Getting angry, and expressing that anger, without making any effort to control or manage your reaction only makes it more likely to happen again. Venting *intensifies* krodha and lays down the neurological foundation for the vritti. Repeated expression of krodha solidifies the neurological pathways of this experience in the brain, laying down the wiring for the reaction to repeat itself and create a cycle of behaviour. Once krodha becomes habituated, it can change the functioning of the brain.

On the cellular level, there are several neurotransmitters responsible for activating the amygdala. These include norepinephrine, dopamine, serotonin, acetylcholine and glutamate. If neurons in the amygdala receive stress signals continuously from the same stimulus, whether that be financial problems, workplace hassles, or relationship issues, they become sensitized to that stimuli. The interaction between the senses and the mind, when stressful and repeated, creates a pathway of neurological behaviour between the senses and the vritti of krodha. The sms from the person who is bugging you goes straight to the amygdala and you live in a state of stress and krodha.

41

There is a direct relationship between krodha and the neurotransmitter serotonin. Repeated and habitual krodha significantly lowers levels of serotonin. Serotonin helps to reduce the krodha response by facilitating neural circuits between the limbic system and the cortex. This makes it easier for the prefrontal cortex to intervene and restrain the anger response. Low levels of serotonin result in weaker connections between these two parts of the brain, so logical intervention and reasoning becomes much more difficult.

80 to 90 percent of the human body's total serotonin is used in regulating the functioning of the gut muscles, facilitating the contraction of the intestines. The remainder regulates appetite, sleep and mood contributing to feelings of wellbeing and happiness. Feeling stressed and angry reduces levels of serotonin which affects appetite and also the body's ability to digest food and obtain proper nutrients. In addition, the stomach is disturbed by the chemical changes in the body and reacts by producing too much acid, leading to gastric ulcers and acid reflux.

Some people respond to this chemical imbalance by eating excessively, and making poor nutritional choices resulting in weight gain and associated health problems. Other people experience loss of appetite and are unable to eat and digest properly. The problem is that serotonin is released when food is consumed. If intake is reduced, then the levels of serotonin in the body also reduce. This then affects the ability of the brain to restrain krodha and the cycle continues. The hungrier you are, the angrier you will become.

Krodha also causes the release of cortisol, the stress hormone. Cortisol affects the cells in a part of the brain called the hippocampus, which is the part linked with learning and long-term memory. Exposure to large amounts of cortisol can cause memory impairment by damaging the cells leading to lowered cognitive functionality and memory loss. A state of physiological and mental alertness is vital for efficient memory. Moderate levels of alertness and arousal

42

help the brain to learn and enhance memory, concentration and performance. However, when arousal exceeds that optimum level, it makes it more difficult for new memories to form.

> Emotion is a motive power like the steam of an engine. It helps you in your evolution. Had it not been for the presence of emotion you would have passed into a state of passivity or inertia. It gives a push for action or motion. It is a blessing. But you must not become a prey to emotions. You must not allow the emotions to rule over you. You must not allow them to bubble out. You must purify and calm the surging emotions.
>
> —*Swami Sivananda Saraswati*

Emotions are generated through and processed by different structures in the brain. There is a difference between emotional processing through the amygdala and that of the neocortex region. The amygdala area of the brain is linked to the senses and deals with sensory data. It passes through the amygdala on its route from the sensory organs along certain neural pathways towards the limbic forebrain. The processing that takes place in the amygdala is rapid, minimal and evaluative processing of the emotional significance of sensory data. It is here that krodha is triggered by sensorial input. The neurological spike of that impulse lasts less than two seconds.

After two seconds, if the reaction of krodha is amplified, it means the emotional processing of thoughts and memories has also become involved. Emotional stimulus from thoughts or memories also generate emotional content and this is discerned and processed by the brain when the information is relayed from the thalamus to the neocortex. Therefore, the neurological experience of krodha demonstrates two distinct processes. The first is caused by emotional reaction to sensory input that generates the feeling of dwesha. The second cause is not dependent upon sensory input, but stems from thoughts, thinking patterns, assumptions and expectations. It is here, in the realm of the mind, that krodha is generated through raga that forms *kama*, or desire.

Anger gains strength by repetition. If it is checked then and there, man gains immense strength of will. When anger is controlled, it becomes transmuted into spiritual energy that can move the three worlds. Just as heat or light is changed into electricity, so also anger becomes changed into ojas. Energy takes another form. Energy is wasted enormously when one gets angry.

—*Swami Sivananda Saraswati*

Psychological experience of krodha

In the *Bhagavad Gita*, Sri Krishna explains krodha as a result of the interaction between the mind, senses and the objects of the senses. The focus is on the interrelationship between kama and krodha, and therefore the description given discusses attachment, desire and the frustration of desire that manifests as krodha. From this perspective, the patterns of thought and mental conditioning that support and contribute to the vritti are highlighted.

Krodha begins through contact between the mind and sense objects and that contact creates attachment. Attachment leads to kama or desire, and kama leads to krodha. (2:62):

ध्यायतो विषयान्पुंस: सङ्गस्तेषूपजायते ।
सङ्गात्सञ्जायते काम: कामात्क्रोधोऽभिजायते ॥

Dhyaayato vishayaanpumsah sangasteshoopajaayate;
Sangaatsanjaayate kaamah kaamaatkrodho'bhijaayate.

When a man thinks of the objects, attachment for them arises; from attachment desire is born; from desire anger arises.

44

Attachment indicates the entanglement of mind with the objects of the senses that follows the reaction of raga. Once entanglement takes place, the senses and the sense objects have no further role in krodha. It is raga and attachment that transmute into the vritti of krodha. This transmutation takes place in the mind, and krodha becomes a physiological and psychological experience. This entire progression has also been described in the *Bhagavad Gita* (2:63):

क्रोधाद्भवति सम्मोह: सम्मोहात्स्मृतिविभ्रम: ।
स्मृतिभ्रंशाद् बुद्धिनाशो बुद्धिनाशात्प्रणश्यति ॥

Krodhaadbhavati sammohah sammohaatsmritivibhramah;
Smritibhramshaad buddhinaasho buddhinaashaatpranashyati.

From anger comes delusion, from delusion the loss of memory; from loss of memory the destruction of discrimination; from the destruction of discrimination he perishes.

Here Sri Krishna explains that the vritti of krodha has a particular pattern, shape and field of influence. When that takes hold in the mind, an experience of mental delusion follows. The mind is constantly receiving information from the senses, but it will construct and interpret data according to the dominant influence at the time. If the dominant influence is krodha then that vritti overrides the normal behaviour of the mind. Krodha determines the interpretation of sensory information. Objective assessment is lost and any stimulus, whether real or imaginary, can be identified as a threat, or a frustration of desire. The key point is that the neurological and physiological response of anger will be the same even if the threat is imaginary. Differentiation between the objective reality and the subjective perception is lost. When a person can no longer tell the difference between events and what they think about those events, they have lost contact with reality.

This statement of the *Bhagavad Gita* is substantiated by the physiological experience of extreme anger. The condition of high physical and mental arousal significantly decreases the ability to concentrate. Due to the increase in cortisol, the left hemisphere of the brain becomes more stimulated. The field of attention narrows significantly and the entire cognitive capacity is focused on the target identified. It is very difficult to divert the cognitive energy towards anything other than the immediate situation and the person is unable to reason or think properly. Unlike other negative emotions such as sadness and fear, which can induce a state of pratyahara and promote analytical thinking, krodha actually deludes the mind and confounds the intellect.

Not able to differentiate between internal and external causes, a person who is angry will blame another person, situation or circumstance for his or her misery. Krodha makes people less trusting and slower to attribute good qualities to others and this leads to misunderstanding of other people in social situations. Habitually angry people think others are being hostile when they are not and make the wrong conclusions about their intentions. In a social interaction, reliable sources of information like body language, gestures and nuance can be ignored. Only those things that reinforce the belief that the other person is hostile will be noticed. Less attention is given to detail and more attention to the superficial because the superficial aspects of interactions can be manipulated to suit assumptions and judgements.

Angry people will demonstrate correspondence bias, the tendency to blame a person's behaviour more on their nature than on circumstances. In place of objective evaluation that takes into account the circumstances and relevant factual information, emotional judgements are made. Emotional judgements make it much easier to form negative connotations about a person's nature. When making judgements angry people tend to rely more on stereotypes, as well as past events, that aroused similar experiences. In inter-group relationships, krodha makes people think in more negative and prejudiced terms about other groups of people. An angry person also tends to anticipate other events that might cause them anger. This is projection of krodha into the future, creating the perception of hostility where none exists.

Once this delusion sets in, the objective memory is lost. This is why it is difficult to remember details of explosive arguments. When krodha takes the form of extreme arousal and aggression, the ability to remember clearly and accurately is severely compromised due to chemical imbalance and physiological changes. The experience of any intense emotion conditions the awareness and mind to vibrate at a particular frequency. Krodha has its own frequency. Kama has its own frequency. *Lobha*, or greed, has its own frequency. Love has another frequency. When in the grips of a vritti, the mind is vibrating with that frequency.

Like a tuning fork, it becomes sensitized to and attracts the same frequency in memories, circumstances and other people. When people are in a certain emotional state, they are more aware of and can easily remember and connect with other circumstances and things charged with the same emotion. Scientific research also concurs on this point. Mood congruence refers to the ability to retrieve memories related to the mood currently being experienced. If you are angry, you will easily and more accurately be able to retrieve information relating to past experiences of anger.

Mood dependent retrieval is a type of context-dependent memory. This means the retrieval of information is more effective when the emotional state at the time of retrieval is similar to the emotional state at the time of encoding. The probability of remembering an event can be enhanced by evoking the emotional state experienced during its initial processing. Angry people will remember other instances of anger easily, but it will be much more difficult to remember and access memories of other emotional states, including positive experiences. This is what Sri Krishna refers to as the loss of memory caused by krodha. It is like a computer hard drive when the files are corrupted. The memory that remains is a corrupted file that cannot be read or understood properly.

Not only is there loss of actual memory and impaired ability to remember, but krodha results in the inability to connect with positive memories. If the ability to remember accurately the positive, supportive and uplifting experiences of life is lost, then *buddhi*, or the intellect, is affected. Intellect is always guided by memory. It is the memory that informs the decisions, logic, reasoning and wisdom of intellect. Without memory there is no reference for buddhi to use. Once the ability to connect with positive memory is compromised, then it is the negative connections and content of life that colours the entire functioning of buddhi. When the hard drive that buddhi accesses is only showing files sorted according to memories that are congruent with aggression, hostility and rage, the ability to discriminate is gone.

Discrimination means the ability to observe objectively from different angles, to evaluate the pros and cons, anticipate consequences, and decide on the correct and appropriate course of action. To discern and discriminate requires options and the ability to view things from different perspectives. Once krodha dominates and destroys the memory, anger becomes the only perspective. Finally, from the loss of discrimination, the individual perishes, because the ability to connect with the positive in life has gone.

> Anger acts as a boomerang because it injures the man who becomes angry. It comes back to the angry man and does harm to him. Therefore, control anger by *kshama* or forgiveness, love, enquiry and service.
>
> —*Swami Sivananda Saraswati*

Social impact of krodha

Krodha destroys the cohesion of society. The social impact of krodha is seen not only in anger and violence, but also in the fear, insecurity and chaos that it creates. By its very nature the vritti is unpredictable. Angry people can explode at any time. Unpredictability causes instability and insecurity in relationships. Where there is instability and insecurity it is very difficult to maintain trust. Trust, respect and a sense of shared values are the foundation for secure relationships and social harmony. In the family unit secure relationships and trust are especially important factors in the emotional development of children. Trust and security are destroyed by the unpredictability of krodha.

Krodha reduces the intimacy within personal relationships. Angry people are less likely to have healthy supportive relationships and tend to have fewer friends. Hostile people are also more likely to suffer erratic mood swings, depression, and to become verbally or physically abusive towards others, alienating family and friends. Venting anger and frustration with words or actions makes the situation much worse, especially for those who are in the immediate path of the attack. Even partners and other family members tend to be more guarded and less able to relax in their interactions with angry people.

> All evil qualities proceed from anger. If you control anger, all evil qualities will vanish by themselves.
>
> —*Swami Sivananda Saraswati*

The most extreme expression of krodha is violence, and debates continue as to whether or not society has actually become more violent. Definitely the social picture of today describes a changed world – one in which the security of the 1950s has given way to a violent society characterized by drug wars, robbery and killing on neighbourhood streets, and violence in school corridors. The impact of the increase in violent content in entertainment, computer games, apps, movies and media is significant. Studies suggest that exposure to violent media increases the likelihood of aggressive behaviour in the short and long term as well as encouraging hostile perceptions and attitudes. Repetitive viewing also desensitizes individuals to violent content.

Research has consistently shown a correlation between TV violence and escalating aggression and social anxiety, and negative impacts upon real-world behaviour.

Exposure to krodha in any form impacts most significantly upon children. A major exposure is through television and digital games. Research on the effect of TV violence on children points to the inescapable conclusion that viewing media violence is related to increases in aggressive attitudes, values, and behaviour. Exposure to violence is among the most detrimental experiences children can have, affecting how they think, feel and act. Children who see or experience violence around them are more likely to use violence as they grow older and into adulthood.

The impact of krodha upon social relationships and society is undeniably negative. Negative emotions are the basis of destructive interactions and toxic connections between people. Negative emotions develop societies based on fear, inequality and domination. Positive emotions are the connections that provide support, care, respect, appreciation, friendship and love. Positive emotions increase and gain in strength when reciprocated through connection with others. Positive connections create positive relationships, positive relationships foster strong, stable, nurturing family units and systems; stable families create cohesive communities and cohesive communities forge the way for peaceful, harmonious, creative societies and cultural development.

Man has reached the moon but he is incapable of bridging the rift between his neighbour and himself. Blessed is this man of the scientific age. It is this ignorance which has to be removed.

—*Swami Sivananda Saraswati*

5

Krodha and the Gunas

Take care of your thoughts. Then the actions will take
care of themselves. Action follows thoughts. Acts create
habits. Habit creates character. Character creates destiny.
So your destiny is in your hands. Shut out all negative
thoughts. Allow good thoughts. We are what our thoughts
have made us and will be what they make us.

—*Swami Sivananda Saraswati*

The purpose of yoga is spiritual evolution, and spiritual
evolution begins in the simplest way, by making the effort to
bring about a qualitative change in life. This change begins
when we start working with the six negative conditions to
overcome and transform these obstacles that thwart our
progress and evolution in life. From the yogic perspective
the six conditions of kama, krodha, lobha, moha, mada,
matsarya are all expressions of the mind belonging to the
dimensions of tamas and rajas.

Rajas and tamas are both self-oriented and self-centric
states of consciousness. It is only in the sattwic dimension
that selflessness emerges and influences the consciousness.
Tamas indicates a self-oriented state of consciousness which
is vibrating at the lowest frequency. The dimension of
tamoguna is the physical, material dimension, in which the
sensorial and sensual inputs and influence predominate.

Tamasic krodha is the passive covert response of anger that tries to justify one's own position, to gather support and a feeling of security through concealed means.

Rajas is also a self-oriented state of consciousness but it pertains to the mental and emotional realms of experience and the frequency is different. The rajoguna dimension is where self-assertion, self-image and comparison take over and the mind revolves around assessing whether the situation or circumstance is good for me or bad for me. Rajasic krodha is overt reactive aggression, characterized by physical, verbal and mental outbursts directed at the person or situation.

The different systems, practices and techniques of yoga aim to reduce the influence of tamas and rajas upon the mind and increase the experience of sattwa. Understanding the influence of tamas, rajas and sattwa is a process of self-analysis. The influence of the six conditions is most detrimental when tamas and rajas predominate. In order to limit their influences and eventually transform the negative quality into a positive expression we need to work through the gunas. The starting point is to observe and analyze the expression of tamas and rajas in daily life, the traits of thought, speech, behaviour and interactions. Habits, preferences, attitudes and thinking patterns indicate the influence of the gunas and the impact of the six conditions on the personality. Once you are able to observe and identify the guna that is interacting with krodha, you can apply the correct antidote.

The antidote is the opposite quality that has to be introduced little by little, again and again. Each time you observe the negative, add the opposite positive quality. This begins to neutralize the effect of the negative reaction upon the personality. It is not that krodha disappears, but the influence that it has upon the personality gradually decreases, the influence of the positive quality increases. Two things happen simultaneously. The negative and restricting condition of mind is managed and the positive and uplifting condition of mind is enhanced. The effort you make to move towards sattwa by connecting with the opposite quality lessens the grip of rajas and tamas. When this is perfected, a transformation of personality takes place.

To help sadhakas in this process of transformation, Swami Niranjanananda has identified different lifestyle yamas and niyamas to be used in the management of the gunas. Although krodha is the focus, it is the influence of the gunas that is being moderated and transformed through the use of yama and niyama. These positive qualities and expressions have been selected because of their opposite relationship to the six conditions. The yamas are conditions and attitudes of mind and the niyamas are the expression and performance of that positive quality. Yamas represent the unity of mind and heart, and niyamas represent the harmonious expression of that unity through the hands.

TAMASIC KRODHA

Of tamas, Sri Krishna says in the *Bhagavad Gita* (14:8):

तमस्त्वज्ञानजं विद्धि मोहनं सर्वदेहिनाम् ।
प्रमादालस्यनिद्राभिस्तन्निबध्नाति भारत ॥

Tamastwajnaanajam viddhi mohanam sarvadehinaam;
Pramaadaalasyanidraabhis tannibadhnaati bhaarata.

Know tamas to be born of ignorance, deluding all embodied beings. It binds through carelessness, laziness and sleep, O Arjuna.

It is the tamoguna which promotes identification with the body. The entire awareness and perception is limited and conditioned by this identification. Self-centric identification combined with a need for security and gratification is the characteristic condition of tamas. Consequently, the activities of the senses, desire, attention and energy are directed outside only in relation to oneself. The outside world only exists in relation to oneself. In tamoguna there is no ability to discriminate between right and wrong and there is a tendency towards mental projection and fantasy, indulgent thinking and behaviour. When the fantasy is not attainable, evasion and withdrawal techniques come to the fore, and the effort is made to cut the connection with the outside world.

Projection

The influence of tamas on the mind is always negative. When tamas predominates in the personality, the negative response to situations and circumstances is highlighted and strengthened. The influence of tamas reinforces the reaction of dwesha and this is projected upon other people, circumstances and situations, hurling the inner negativity outwards. There is always something to complain about. Life is coloured in darkness and gloom and the beauty of the moment, the effort made, the positive intention and aspiration is never seen or acknowledged. Instead the attention is entirely focused on and devoted to finding something to complain about, something to criticize and highlight as incorrect or substandard. In the state of tamas the glass will always be half-empty. The fact that the glass is also half-full will never be acknowledged or emphasized.

Tamasic krodha originates from the reaction of dwesha and is reinforced by the negativity of tamas. The binding nature of tamas holds onto the reaction of krodha long after the situation has past and entrenches this negativity by dredging up memories. The negative is never forgotten and the mind is constantly charged by feelings of anger and resentment about things that happened years ago. The mind grinds itself repeatedly on the stone of its own negativity, with criticism, gossip, backstabbing and fault-finding.

The tamasic capability for mental projection is so powerful that despite it being glaringly apparent to everyone else, the person can be unaware that they are expressing a negative form of krodha. Instead of recognizing their own feelings of anger and negativity, a person experiencing tamasic krodha will cast themselves in the role of victim and blame everyone else around them for their own misery. Nobody likes them because they are unpleasant to be around, yet they blame everyone else for their loneliness. This can make it one of the most difficult types of krodha to control or even identify.

Experience

The experience of tamasic krodha is a reaction to a perceived threat to one's sense of security and stability. Everything is seen from the most negative perspective possible, even a smile and cheerful greeting will be deliberately misconstrued. The feeling of insecurity underlies tamasic krodha, and the response of dwesha is magnified resulting in the desire to withdraw, avoid and sabotage. The focus is on underhanded manipulation rather than confrontation, constantly provoking insecurity and unhappiness in people, but staying on the sidelines and inciting others into confrontation.

The experience of tamasic krodha deliberately sabotages and undermines constructive effort. By withdrawing from direct communication there is an experience of power for the individual as they set about sabotaging other people's happiness, creativity and success. This ability to detrimentally influence and destroy someone else's emotional happiness makes the tamasic krodha person feel secure and happy, but this is only temporary. When the insecurity levels rise, the whole projection begins again. Being around tamasic krodha is like being on an emotional roller coaster. The constant blaming and criticism makes everyone else feel uncomfortable, dispirited and sad without understanding why.

Expression

Tamasic krodha is expressed in subtle ways characterized by rigidity, immobility and obstruction. It is not the violent explosive aggression but a constant subterranean current of negativity and resentment that has different degrees and gradients of expression. This negative expression of krodha often expresses in silent and sullen behaviour and grumpy, sulky, gloomy and sour moods. Verbally tamasic krodha is expressed as sarcasm, subtle insults, mimicry, under-the-breath mutterings, pointed silence or veiled mockery. When a person chooses to reply to an innocent comment, question, or remark in a negative way, that is tamasic krodha. A sullen person will not respond positively, no matter how much effort is made to encourage them out of the mood, they will not smile, even when someone tells a joke and everybody else is laughing.

More elaborate means of expression include emotional blackmail, false tearfulness, feigning illness, secretive behaviour, stockpiling resentments that are expressed behind people's backs, putting people down, gossiping, anonymous complaints, cyber bullying and hate speech. Non-verbal cues include fake smiles, eye rolling, avoiding eye contact, looking the other way when being spoken to or giving the cold shoulder. Completely ignoring another person, refusing to respond to questions from that person, and refusing to acknowledge their presence are examples of non-verbal expression. Also included is behaviour that blocks creativity, cooperation and communication, such as avoidance, arriving late, purposefully performing badly or chronic procrastination. Actions that are negative, harmful and obstructive to oneself are also expressions of tamasic krodha. They can manifest as emotional or physical self-harm, including eating disorders, substance abuse and obsessive behaviour.

> Krodha is a vritti or modification that arises in the mind-lake when the two gunas, rajas and tamas, predominate. It is a rajoguna vritti. Some take it as a tamoguna vritti. It is a wave of unpleasant feeling that arises from the antahkarana, when one gets displeased with another. It is in other words, a modification of desire or passion. Just as milk is changed into curd, so also desire changes into anger. It is the most formidable enemy of peace, knowledge and devotion.
>
> —*Swami Sivananda Saraswati*

Kshama – forgiveness

Swami Niranjanananda has given one yama and one niyama for the management of krodha. The yama is *kshama* or forgiveness. Kshama is the attitude and quality of mind that lessens the grip and removes the blockages of tamasic krodha. Kshama is a process of release, letting go of negativity, while tamasic krodha is a state of entrenchment, holding on to, repeating and reliving negativity. In kshama you learn to let go of the attitudes, perceptions, memories and feelings of harm or wrongdoing that you hold on to in relation to people and circumstances in life.

Kshama is releasing the feeling of blame and resentment for things that have happened in the past. This is important because tamas is a mental state that is conditioned by the past and is therefore a major impediment to any form of progress and evolution in life. Tamasic conditioning does not relate to the present or the future, except through the memories of the past. Tamasic krodha relives the impressions and experiences of the past by projecting them into the present, in the form of blame, accusation, resentment, bitterness, antipathy and hostility.

Kshama is the opposite, it brings you into the present with the intention to release the past. Kshama is a process whereby you clear out the memories, the *pratyayas*, the impressions of the past. The old hurts, resentments, betrayals, disappointments and frustrations that sit in the mind and reinforce the state of tamas have to be released to free the mind from the vritti of krodha. Tamasic krodha is catalyzed by these past impressions and when activated it enters the mind and clouds the entire perception, attitude and experience with the darkness of the hurt that you felt in the past.

Unlike rajasic krodha that can be utilized to change a situation and catalyze a different experience, tamasic krodha reinforces the previous condition and with repetition cements that experience deeper and deeper into the mind and personality. You live in the past, and in the worst possible version of the past, feeling alienated, alone and hurt. In this way tamasic krodha is a self-fulfilling prophecy, because the sullen, defensive and hostile behaviour provokes responses of aversion and dislike from people. The feeling of being isolated, hurt and victimized is reinforced. Tamasic krodha keeps you chained to the suffering of the past and forced to repeat it again and again without release.

Kshama is the way out of this cycle of negativity and resentment. Kshama makes a positive connection in the mind. Instead of connecting to the past hurt or betrayal, kshama connects you to a state and experience of openness and freedom. It brings with it the ability to make choices about how to react and respond in the present moment to create a better future. Kshama is not merely a sentimental concept, nor is it about the other person. Kshama is about your own mind and generating an experience of pratyahara so that the negativity and heaviness of the old impressions can be released. The *asakti* or attachment to the past has to be released. It is this asakti that reinforces the heaviness of tamas and the strength of the associated vrittis like krodha. When you express and feel kshama, a natural state of security and happiness is experienced, because the mental condition is optimistic and positive. With kshama it is not the suffering and feeling of pain that defines who you are, it is the decision to live in joy, happiness and peace that defines you.

Kshama is a process. It doesn't happen immediately, it takes time and repeated effort. It begins by realizing that negativity only hurts yourself. There is a saying that resentment is like drinking poison and waiting for the other person to die. You are consuming your own negativity through resentment, bitterness and smouldering anger every time that memory is triggered, every time you see that person, or remember what happened. But somehow the expectation is that this negativity will make the other person suffer and pay for how they have hurt you. It is illogical. Forgiveness does not mean that you forget or condone what happened. It means that you recognize the harm that krodha does to yourself, and release the tamasic grip of your own negativity.

To practise a strong intention or *sankalpa* is necessary. This helps direct the energy of the mind into the process of choosing the positive over the negative. Sankalpa helps create a shift in identity that propels you out of the gravitational pull of the tamasic mindset and releases the grasp of krodha. The negative thinking, complaining, blaming and judging lessens and a different perspective opens up that is lighter, open to creative possibilities and positivity. Over time, as krodha is curtailed and the conditioning of tamas is eroded, a more objective understanding develops. Rather than making judgements and criticisms based on personality, objectivity allows you to understand another person's perspective and circumstances. Kshama encourages understanding and acceptance and is the first step to peace in your own heart and in the world.

> What does it mean to forgive? If you don't empty your bowels for a day, you suffer; you need to eliminate everything from the stomach regularly. In the same way, you have to take out the rubbish from the mind. In meditation when you are discovering the cause of your happiness and unhappiness, the person who has triggered these states will appear in your consciousness. At that moment, visualize the person clearly and forgive them. Just finish the negative emotion, take it out from your heart, clear it. The next morning give a big smile to the other person and say, "Good morning. How are you today?"
>
> —*Swami Niranjanananda Saraswati*

Namaskara – greeting

The niyama that compliments kshama is namaskara. *Namaskara* refers to the action of salutation, when you greet and acknowledge others. Namaskara is the action that accompanies humility and represents softness of mind and heart. In tamasic krodha namaskara is the nail used to break the self-oriented perspective that keeps the mind and personality stuck. Tamasic krodha is expressed through avoidance, sulking, ignoring, not engaging and refusing to communicate and namaskara imposes the opposite expression through greeting and salutation. Namaskara breaks the hard shell of tamas and the first ray of light penetrates into the darkness of the insecure and self-oriented ego. To counter the insecurity, resentments and subterranean hostility of tamasic krodha, namaskara creates a connection with your own positivity. This is the first step. Only by connecting with your own positivity can you truly practise namaskara and greet everyone with a smile and good feeling.

It is the positive sentiments within that are given expression in namaskara. Instead of reliving past hurts and expecting something to happen to make up for it, and being bitter and resentful when that doesn't happen, by practising namaskara you have something to give. There is a mental shift from the perception of absence to existence, from negative to positive. The more often namaskara is practised, the stronger the internal connection with the positive becomes, and the influence of tamasic krodha decreases. Instead of expressing krodha through bitterness, grumpiness and sour, sulky moods, the positive aspects of your personality begin to shine forth, and happiness and joy expresses in the act of namaskara.

> It is the connection with humility which connects us with individuals and with the cosmos, and then we understand what our role is in life, for which we have taken birth. Is it to spend half of life in anger, strife and hatred? Is it for that reason that we have taken birth? Or to learn to connect with harmony by changing ourself, by disconnecting or disassociating with ego when not necessary, and connecting with something different for fulfilment and satisfaction in life.
>
> —*Swami Niranjanananda Saraswati*

RAJASIC KRODHA

In the *Bhagavad Gita,* Sri Krishna explains rajoguna as the desire for enjoyment and attachment (14:7):

रजो रागात्मकं विद्धि तृष्णास ङ्गसमुद्भवम् ।
तन्निबध्नाति कौन्तेय कर्मस ङ्गेन देहिनम् ।

Rajo raagaatmakam viddhi trishnaasangasamudbhavam;
Tannibadhnaati kaunteya karmasangena dehinam.

Know the nature of rajas to be passion, the source of craving and attachment. Arjuna, it binds the embodied one through attachment to action.

Sri Krishna also says that both kama and krodha are born out of rajoguna (3:37):

काम एष क्रोध एष रजोगुणसमुद्भव: ||
महाशनो महापाप्मा विद्ध्येनमिह वैरिणम् ||

Kaama esha krodha esha rajo-guna-samudbhavah
Mahaashano mahaa-paapmaa viddhyenam iha vairinam.

It is desire, it is anger, born of the quality of rajas,
All devouring, all sinful, know this as the enemy.

From this statement we learn that two types of rajasic krodha exist. The first type of rajasic krodha is based on kama which has been frustrated. When the power of rajoguna is attached to the aspect of desire, the need for self-gratification in the personality is strengthened. If that desire is not fulfilled, if the need for self-gratification is frustrated, then rajasic krodha is the result. Rajasic krodha is a volatile, aggressive and dynamic expression, and it is the power and dynamism of the rajoguna that fuels this reaction. This is seen in people who feel they have been obstructed or cheated, denied what should be theirs. The reaction of krodha expresses as a desire to destroy another person's happiness and have revenge at any cost.

61

The second type of rajasic krodha is caused by the inter-action of rajas and kama expressing as desire for domination. The power and dynamism of rajas is attached to kama and krodha becomes the vehicle of the rajasic nature. The vritti created by this combination has a very strong influence on the mind and personality. The important point is that no obstruction to the fulfilment of desire is required in order for krodha to manifest. Krodha is an integral part and natural expression of the personality. This is seen in people who always need to be the best and dominate others, who manipulate situations and circumstances to their own advantage and other people's detriment. Krodha is the method to attain this supremacy.

Projection

The influence of rajas on the mind is dynamic and self-assertive. When rajoguna predominates the dominating and superior ego identity is projected. Rajasic krodha is the reaction projected onto a situation or person when expectations, ambitions and desires are frustrated. When a desire is not gratified, a volatile and angry reaction explodes against the perceived obstacle. The key word here is perceived, because it is the mental conditioning that is responsible for the projection of rajasic krodha. The justification links the response of krodha to an external cause, but this is the projection, not the reality.

Specific patterns of thought are involved in the pro-jection of rajasic krodha and emotional reasoning is a key indicator. Emotional reasoning is what happens when perception, interpretation and understanding begin from an emotional reaction and are not qualified by any objec-tive reasoning. Events, circumstances and other people are interpreted subjectively according to how the person feels at the time. Emotional reasoning leads to an irra-tional perspective of reality, and people often misinterpret normal events and communication. Emotional reasoning also leads to unreasonable expectations in which people make subjective assessments that do not encompass the reality of the situation and impose unrealistic demands upon others.

Everything is about me and how I am being treated. People with strong emotionally based reasoning often become irritated at innocent things other people say or do. They perceive these things as attacks on themselves and the corresponding reaction is rajasic krodha, reactive aggression that strikes back. In these instances, there is no logic because the experience is subjective and has no objective basis.

Experience

Rajasic krodha has a wide spectrum of experience. Irritation comes up without any real provocation and is felt when people and events are not happening in congruence with subjective opinions and expectations. Irritation is like discomfort and agitation in the mind that is then transmitted to the body. The experience of irritation is the precursor. From irritation comes dissatisfaction. If not contained, the next experience is frustration, where the agitated feeling increases, becoming hotter and more difficult to control. Once there is a sustained feeling of frustration if this cannot be curtailed, the result is a reactive outburst of anger inflicted on everyone around.

Stress lowers the tolerance for frustration. The lower the frustration tolerance the more likely it is that normal things are interpreted as threats. When someone feels they are being threatened, either emotionally, mentally, physically, then the experience of rajasic krodha is pure reactive aggression in any form. The desire to assert oneself and to dominate takes over. The urge to retaliate, the desire for vengeance, the impetus to cause harm and violence are the extreme experiences of rajasic krodha.

Anger shreds everybody to pieces, that is the expression and behaviour of anger. When you are angry with someone what do you do? You slash them like an animal would. Anger is the uncontrollable instinct to tear someone down. The antidote for this is the yama, *kshama* or forgiveness.

—*Swami Niranjanananda Saraswati*

Expression

Rajasic krodha is a desire for power that is expressed negatively, in different manifestations of the dwesha reaction. Through expression the person seeks to dominate others and establish their own superiority. The continuum begins with not listening, talking over people's heads, expressing mistrust, not delegating, judgements, manipulation, lies and blaming. When people blame others for their own mistakes, or for their own negativity and lack of emotional management, rajasic krodha is dominant in the personality at that moment. More direct and heightened expressions of rajasic krodha are found in behaviour and speech that is insulting, taunting, threatening, bullying, persecuting and abusive. This culminates in rage, aggression and violence.

> Passion is the root and anger the stem. You will have to destroy the root (passion) first. Then the stem (anger) will die by itself. A passionate man is more angry.

—*Swami Sivananda Saraswati*

A key indicator of this type of krodha is unpredictability and inconsistency of behaviour. Explosive rages over minor frustrations, attacking people indiscriminately, dispensing unjust punishment, inflicting difficulties and harm on others for the sake of it are all examples. What is okay today may become the biggest outrage tomorrow and the cause for heads to roll. There is no consistency or systematic objectivity in behaviour because the expression of rajasic krodha stems from frustration of desires and desires are constantly changing.

The mind refuses to think of itself, but is ever eager to think of others. If you analyze its vagaries, you will find that it does so only in order to find others' faults (or even imagine them) and as a consequence feel supremely happy in the thought 'I am superior to others'. If, on the other hand, man learns to see only good in others, to think well of others, if he must think of them; and to concentrate more and more on his own self, to find out the evils that lurk within him, and to try to eradicate them there would be peace everywhere.

—*Swami Sivananda Saraswati*

Kshama – forgiveness

The yama of kshama is also important in the management and transformation of rajasic krodha. It is the involvement of rajoguna with krodha that creates hostile, volatile, aggressive and abusive reactions. While tamasic krodha harms oneself, rajasic krodha causes the most harm to other people and damages relationships. In tamasic krodha the quality of kshama is used to break the conditioning that holds on to past hurt. That is tamas. In rajasic krodha there is also a need to forgive others for perceived slights and offences to which the rajasic ego has taken objection, but the target is different. In tamasic krodha it is the hard shell of self-protection that has to crack and in rajasic krodha the armour of arrogance, pride and superciliousness has to be broken.

When you are hurt, insulted or wronged, this feeling takes over the mind and the suffering is highlighted. Rajasic krodha is the reaction that surges up to compensate for this feeling of being hurt. The vritti of krodha corrupts the operation of buddhi and blocks the access to *smritti* or memory. The previous experiences of love, support and friendship you may have shared with that person are all forgotten. All the times that person has helped you are forgotten and only the negative memory remains. The person you are blaming for your own suffering becomes the enemy. Resentment and anger spirals into thoughts of aggression and revenge. Each thought gives birth to a new hostility and another aggressive desire. Without buddhi to intervene and without access to the files and records stored in chitta there is not much hope for navigating out of this downward spiral.

This is the vritti of rajasic krodha. The influence of rajas propels a succession of outbursts and reactions that exacerbate the situation and eventually destroy the relationship. Kshama breaks this cycle. When you make the effort to forgive the other person, you open the door for the other memories and experiences to come in. You open the door to the positive. Kshama breaks the cycle of rajasic krodha by kick-starting buddhi back into operation. Deciding to forgive and drop the associated negativity releases the grip of krodha on the mind and buddhi regains access to memories of positive interaction and shared happiness.

In rajasic krodha, the practice of kshama expands to include awareness of the pain of others. The understanding deepens and a new realization dawns. The experience of hurt, injury, insult and offence is not limited to yourself. The awareness expands to encompass not only your pain and suffering but also that of others. In moments of anger, frustration and hostility your words, sentiments and behaviour have hurt others. Just as you have been hurt through the anger of others, so also have others been hurt by your anger. The experience is the same, except the self-oriented, limited and conditioned mind can only feel its own suffering, not the suffering of others. Kshama expands the awareness to encompass a greater mental and emotional sensitivity.

> Even if a man hates you, you must love him. Then only you can realize unity. You must love all. You must love a thief, a drunkard, a rogue and a vagabond. Just as perfume emanates from jasmine, the sweet perfume of love should emanate from you and flow towards all in all directions. Then only is it termed universal love

66

or cosmic love, vishwaprem. Then only you have an expanded heart.

—*Swami Sivananda Saraswati*

Acknowledging the pain of others is the precursor to seeking forgiveness for your actions and behaviour. The process of recognizing the consequences of krodha whether intentional or unintentional opens up the possibility for understanding, empathy and healing. Management of rajasic krodha with kshama means seeking forgiveness and awakening the *sankalpa*, the positive intention, not to cause harm. In meditation, or in periods of quiet reflection and calm, incidents where your behaviour has caused pain and anguish to others will come to the surface of the consciousness and these impressions need to be cleared in order to progress. Through awareness and recognition of the hurt that you have caused, a greater understanding develops. From understanding comes empathy and a real experience of the suffering and pain felt. From empathy arises compassion and the spontaneous desire to seek forgiveness. This is not about guilt or justification, it is a process of expansion of awareness that leads to the beginning of ahimsa, *non-violence* and the sankalpa not to cause harm.

In everything Swami Sivananda did throughout his life, he maintained only one attitude - to do good to everybody. He was never a dictator, and never interfered with his disciples. In fact, he used to touch the feet of his disciples just as a disciple touches his master's feet. Many times I made mistakes, both in my life and in the ashram, as an inmate and as an executive. I thought that he would rebuke me or admonish me, or tell me what was right or wrong, but he never said one word. When I used to go to him, he would never raise the point. He would just say the usual things. He never recognized the mistakes in man. He always used to say that everyone had in him the spark of divinity.

—*Swami Satyananda Saraswati*

Namaskara – greeting

To transform the conditioning of rajasic krodha, the arrogance, pride and hardness of ego have to be cracked. Namaskara is used to pierce this hard shell. The light that penetrates through the cracks made by namaskara is humility. The influence of rajoguna has hardened the nature with arrogance, pride and notions of status and position. This creates the feeling of superiority and the tendency is to look down on people, to consider them inferior, below yourself and not worthy of acknowledgement, let alone respect. Namaskara breaks that conditioning by honouring, greeting and respecting others.

Instead of connecting with your arrogance and condescension by viewing others as beneath you, namaskara means to relate with others as equals. Namaskara means recognizing the other person as worthy of your respect, honour and salutation. From this comes the understanding that we share the same feelings, hopes and desires. Everyone wants to be happy. Nobody wants to suffer. In the spiritual dimension all are equal and united by the thread of divinity that is woven through creation. It is the material mindset that creates and enforces the distinctions of race, caste, creed, gender and class. Breaking these artificial barriers behind which the rajasic ego hides is the sadhana of namaskara.

Work with namaskara to extend your awareness and understanding of the unity that lies in diversity. This is the method to overcome rajasic krodha and defeat the *dvaita bhava*, the feeling of duality, that is a formidable obstacle to spiritual transcendence. Swami Sivananda performed namaskara to everyone, in every station of life, high and low, and made no distinction between the beggar and the sadhu. He regarded women as forms of Devi and mentally performed namaskara before them with the same bhava as he prostrated before the divine. Namaskara removes the experience and perception of duality, expanding awareness and opening the heart to embrace all forms of life as manifestations of the divine.

As an adult I was fond of gymnastics and vigorous exercises. I learnt fencing from a teacher who belonged to a low caste. He was a Harijan. I could go to him only for a few days before I was made to understand that it was unbecoming of a caste-Brahmin to play the student to an untouchable. I thought deeply over the matter. One moment I felt that the God whom we worshipped in the image in my father's worship room had jumped over into the heart of this untouchable. So I immediately went to him with flowers, sweets and clothes and garlanded him, placed flowers at his feet and prostrated myself before him.

—*Swami Sivananda Saraswati*

TRANSFORMATION: EXPERIENCING SATTWA

Regarding the state of sattwa the *Bhagavad Gita* states (14:6):

तत्र सत्त्वं निर्मलत्वात्प्रकाशकमनामयम् ।
सुखस ङ्गेन बध्नाति ज्ञानस ङ्गेन चानघ ॥

Tatra sattwam nirmalatwaat prakaashakam anaamayam;
Sukhasangena badhnaati jnaanasangena chaanagha.

Of these, sattwa, being stainless, luminous and flawless,
binds through self-identification with happiness and
wisdom, Arjuna.

The nature of sattwa is light and knowledge, and it represents a state of purity. When sattwa is predominate, the
ego-identification naturally transcends the selfish, self-
centred perspectives and the influence of the six conditions
is transformed. At the sensorial and physical level there is
purification and restraint. Purification leads to control of
body and speech. Control over body and speech influences
interaction of mind and senses. Information coming from
the senses to the mind does not cause the mind to react with
the feeling of dwesha, rejection and aggression. Because of
the management of raga and dwesha, the mind is steady
and does not swing from desire to anger. Steadiness of
mind leads to balance and equipoise. This is the experience
of *shantata*, balanced awareness, that expands beyond the
gravitational pull of rajas and tamas.

> Be kind to all. Love all. Never hurt the feelings of others.
> Be one with all. Destroy clannishness. Serve all. Respect
> all. Share with others whatever you possess (physical,
> mental and spiritual). Take the whole world as the form
> of Narayana. Bow before the world and everybody with
> folded hands. Give up the ideas of barber, washerman,
> cobbler. Barber is Narayana. Cobbler is Narayana. Bow
> with folded hands before a scavenger and feel that you

are actually bowing to Lord Narayana. Those who are shy can bow mentally. The former one is the best practice to develop equal vision. By the former practice, you can experience the essence of Vedanta, the spirit of equality.

—*Swami Sivananda Saraswati*

In this state of sattwa, the yama of kshama and the niyama of namaskara are the natural expressions of an expanded awareness. Namaskara becomes an expression of an all-encompassing awareness that is experiencing divinity as all-pervading. This is Narayana bhava, beholding, feeling and experiencing the divine in all forms, and namaskara is the expression of that realization. When this is experienced, there is total *samarpan, atmanivedan,* surrender. This is seen in the life of Swami Sivananda. One evening while giving satsang in the ashram, Swami Sivananda was attacked by an unknown assailant. The attempt on his life was unsuccessful, and Swami Sivananda prostrated himself before the assailant and worshipped him as Narayana. His consciousness had completely transcended the distinctions of name and form and he was able to see the divinity even in the person who had come to kill him.

How can you worship God who is in all creatures unless you honour and respect everybody? Treat everybody with respect. View all with an equal eye. Do virtuous actions. Behold the Lord in all beings. Bow to all beings. Have intense and exclusive devotion for the Lord. Centre your thoughts exclusively on Him. Desire nothing, not even moksha. You will soon overcome death and reach the fearless abode of eternal bliss and supreme peace.

—*Swami Sivananda Saraswati*

In this state of awareness, duality is transcended and there is no need to practise kshama, because who is forgiving who? All beings are a manifest form of the ultimate spiritual reality. Kshama opens the heart to feel the pain and suffering of others, as if it was one's own. Pain and suffering are not limited to the self, instead suffering is a shared experience that draws upon the open heart of infinite compassion and love for all beings. From kshama arises *ahimsa*, the state and experience of love in which there is peace and non-violence.

> If you are established in ahimsa, you have attained all virtues. Ahimsa is the pivot. All virtues revolve around ahimsa. The power of ahimsa is greater than the power of intellect. It is easy to develop the intellect, but it is difficult to purify and develop the heart.
>
> —*Swami Sivananda Saraswati*

Ahimsa is not only the idea of non-injury in the physical sense. It is abstinence from causing any pain or harm to any living creature, either by thought, word or deed. It is based upon purification of the body and mind, expansion of awareness and awakening of the heart. The same self is seen in all. By injuring or harming another, you harm yourself. Just as you do not want to be harmed, other beings also do not want to be harmed. Just as you want love, affection and support, so do all beings need love, kindness and compassion. Ahimsa is the mental attitude arising from this realization that transforms hatred in any form into love. The experience of ahimsa represents the perfection of kshama. Ahimsa is positive, unconditioned, cosmic love, not selfish and conditioned love.

Examples of the transcendence of sattwa is seen in the lives of sannyasins, tapasvis, saints and masters. The *Bhagavad Gita* refers to this (5:26):

कामक्रोधवियुक्तानां यतीनां यतचेतसाम् ।
अभितो ब्रह्मनिर्वाणं वर्तते विदितात्मनाम् ॥

*Kaama-krodha-viyuktaanaam yateenaam yata-chetasaam
Abhito brahma-nirvaanam vartate viditaatmanaam.*

Those who are free from desire and anger, and who have subdued their minds and realized themselves – around such austere men lies the beatitude of God.

The qualities of generosity, love, compassion, understanding, peace and harmony become the natural and spontaneous expression of people who have connected with and awakened their inner spiritual nature. When krodha is transformed through the effulgence of sattwa, ahimsa is awakened and peace radiates. In the presence of such a person, enmities cease and all hostilities are given up. In the ashrams of rishis, saints and sages it is said that tigers and deer will drink water together from the same river without any hostility or fear. Beings that are enemies of each other by nature, forget their innate hostility towards one another and co-exist in peace. This is the power of ahimsa. Ahimsa culminates in *brahma nivarnam*, the realization of unity and oneness of life, pure advaitic consciousness.

Guna	Kshama	Namaskara
Tamas	Forgive past hurts Release past impressions Live in the present	Connect with others Counteract insecurity Cultivate inner positivity
Rajas	Let go of desire for revenge Acknowledge pain of others Seek forgiveness for own actions	Control arrogance See others as equal, not lower Awareness of unity
Sattwa	Expanded awareness Experience the suffering of others. Transcending duality.	Narayana bhava Recognizing the divinity that permeates life

Ahimsa is the fundamental quality of seekers after the truth. No self-realization is possible without ahimsa. It is through the practice of ahimsa alone that you can cognize and realize the supreme self or Brahman.

He who practises ahimsa develops strong willpower. In his presence, enmity ceases. In his presence, cobra and frog, cow and tiger, cat and rat, wolf and lamb, will all live together in terms of intimate friendship. In his presence, all hostilities are given up. The term 'hostilities are given up' means that all beings – men, animals, birds and poisonous creatures will approach the practitioner without fear and do no harm to him. Their hostile nature disappears in them in his presence. The rat and the cat, the snake and the mongoose, and other beings that are enemies of each other by nature, give up their hostile feelings in the presence of the yogi who is established in ahimsa. Lions and tigers can never do any harm to such a yogi. Such a yogi can give definite orders to lions and tigers. They will obey. This is *bhuta siddhi*, mastery over the elements, obtainable by the practice of ahimsa. The practice of ahimsa will eventually culminate in the realization of unity and oneness of life, or advaitic, non-dual consciousness. The yogi then enjoys the highest peace, bliss and immortality.

—*Swami Sivananda Saraswati*

Part 3
Sadhana

6

Understanding Krodha
with Jnana Yoga

Human beings are capable of incredible things, of
infinite knowledge and bliss, if they take steps to raise
their level of awareness. Yoga systematically unlocks
the portals of higher consciousness, and leads them
beyond the horizon of limitation, to a greater vision of
fulfilment within this life.

—Swami Niranjanananda Saraswati

Sadhana

Yoga sees the individual not only as a physical body, but also
recognizes the progressively subtler layers of existence, the
subtle bodies formed by the pranas, the mind and mental
energy, the psyche and ultimately the state of pure bliss.
Vedanta also asserts that the essential nature of every being
is divine, and that divinity is experienced as bliss. To come
closer to realizing and experiencing the pure, positive and
luminous nature within we need to learn how to disconnect
from the negative and unhelpful aspects of mind and
emotions. The connection with yoga vidya shows us the
way to improve not only the body, but also our thoughts,
attitudes, feelings and emotions so we can live yoga.
Learning how to live yoga is the challenge of the second
chapter.

For aspirants who are serious about taking the next step, an integral approach to the management of krodha has been given. Observation and analysis of the different expressions of krodha through jnana yoga leads to greater understanding. Hatha yoga helps to reduce the physical and pranic imbalances caused by krodha. Raja yoga techniques refine the interaction between the senses and mind, and with practice, the vritti of anger can be managed. Finally, transformation happens through the lifestyle yama and niyama, the cultivation of positive qualities conducive to the attainment of sattwa. This progression of sadhana leads to the awakening of spirituality in daily life.

> The sadhana, which starts with initiation, should take you toward the management of these six ills, the six enemies. Sri Swamiji has said this even while he was performing the panchagni, "Only one who can survive the five internal fires can survive the five external fires." You have been given many hints, many guidelines on how to deal with yourself, but you have never applied yourself in this direction. You say, "These things are true, yes." Yet you do not apply them to your own life.
>
> —*Swami Niranjanananda Saraswati*

Jnana yoga begins with awareness and objective observation. Objectivity is crucial when examining the influence of the six conditions. It is like treating an illness. When you start feeling sick the first thing you pay attention to are the symptoms. The symptoms are observed objectively and monitored in order to make the correct diagnosis. However, when the illness is of the mind and emotions, objectivity goes out the window. Instead of being able to see clearly the reactions of mind and emotions, the opposite happens. The tamasic and rajasic complexes of inferiority or superiority, projection, justification and associated distorted perspectives take over.

Therefore, swadhyaya begins with the positive intention to connect with truth. Connecting with truth means being able to deal with the negative aspects of your own personality and make the effort to transform them. Don't project individual mental hang-ups and frustrations onto other people or situations. Outward projection of negativity is a waste of time and delays your spiritual evolution. Instead of going forwards, you go backwards. In the spirit of sadhana, maintain the inspiration that sustains your connection to yoga, and have the courage to be honest and sincere.

Once you are able to observe the different experiences and expressions of krodha, it is possible to find the triggers, the circumstances or ways of thinking that catalyze the reaction. Once you identify the trigger, find how to disconnect yourself from that influence. For this two important techniques have been given by Swami Niranjanananda, the first is the SWAN sadhana and the second is Review of the Day. SWAN helps you identify the internal causes of krodha by analyzing and fine-tuning the different components of the personality. Review of the Day helps you become aware of the external circumstances and interactions that trigger the reaction of krodha.

> Drink a little water when you become angry. It will cool the brain and calm the excited nerves. Repeat *Om Shanti* several times. If you find it extremely difficult to control anger, leave the place immediately and take a walk for half an hour.
>
> —*Swami Sivananda Saraswati*

SWAN

SWAN is an acronym and each letter of the acronym stands for a particular aspect of the personality. 'S' stands for the strengths of personality, the positive qualities which are expressed in different ways in different people. 'W' stands for weakness, which indicate the shortcomings in life, the restrictive qualities that do not allow the positivity to manifest. The six friends are all included under weakness. 'A' stands for ambition, representing the drive, motivation and aspiration in life. The last letter 'N' stands for need, the basic requirements of life, whether physical, emotional, social or spiritual.

Take four sheets of paper and sit down in a quiet place. On one sheet of paper, write what you perceive to be your strengths and qualities. On another write what you perceive to be your limitations and weaknesses. On the third write what you perceive to be your aspirations, ambitions and expectations. On the fourth sheet of paper, write your needs, the real needs required to live and be happy.

Now review the list of weaknesses and find the underlying causes of krodha. Without projecting or justifying, try and see where krodha comes from inside. Is your default response to situations negative and coloured by insecurity? Is there a feeling of inferiority that you try to compensate for by aggressive behaviour? If fear dominates, then sensory information will be interpreted as threatening and krodha emerges as a strong sense of self-preservation. Is anger a protective response mechanism? If the weakness is insecurity and fear, that makes you react with hostility and aggression, develop trust, serenity and contentment.

Is the weakness arrogance and pride that makes you strike out in anger and frustration? Analyze that weakness and understand its role in the personality. Identify a strength that can neutralize and counteract that weakness. Explore ways that you can develop and express that strength. For example, if you experience krodha as impatience, develop patience. Critical behaviour can be balanced by objectivity and making the effort to see the positive in situations.

> Anger is an enemy to peace. It is a modification of lust. When a desire is not gratified, a man becomes angry. He loses his memory and understanding. Control anger by the practice of kshama, love, and by killing egoism. When man's conscience is tinged with love, tolerance and goodwill, then the other parts of his personality, his thoughts, his speech and his actions are all bound to

be loving. He will not be greedy; he will not be swayed by lust and anger; he will not be jealous; he will not be arrogant.

—*Swami Sivananda Saraswati*

If you experience krodha as frustration, analyze whether you feel frustrated because a desire is not fulfilled, or when expectations are not fulfilled. To counter frustration from unfulfilled desires, develop sensorial restraint. To neutralize the frustration that comes from unrealistic expectations, change your way of thinking. Develop the ability to understand and empathize with other people instead of projecting your own expectations.

Observe the ambitions in life, the arena of ego expression and projection. Analyze how ambitions are manifesting in your life and creating krodha. If your ambitions relate to profession, krodha will be there in your relationship with colleagues. Rather than interpreting behaviour in terms of your status and getting angry at perceived slights, develop objective understanding and make the effort towards harmonious interactions. Practise namaskara and treat everyone equally. If your ambitions are for social status, krodha will express in relation to your interactions with others. Instead of criticizing and putting others down, restrain the detrimental effect of ambition by resolving not to gossip. Gossip is also a form of violence.

Counter excessive ambition by developing understanding of your actual needs. That which promotes happiness and balance are the characteristics of need, while that which generates negativity and imbalance characterizes ambitions. Learn to differentiate between the two. If the people you work and interact with are stressed, unhappy and if constant strife, drama and difficulty surrounds you, something needs to change. If your interactions are happy and relaxed, and people enjoy working with you, this indicates you have found a balance between need and ambition.

Take a set of weighing scales and on one side place all the negative aspects of life. On the other side, place all the positive things. Which side is heavier? I once conducted this experiment on myself and found that the negative side of the scale far outweighed the positive. One day I asked Sri Swamiji what to do. He told me to totally disregard the negative side, the heavier side. He said, "When you look at how heavy it is you will be anxious about it, and that will make your spirits sink. Instead, try and make the positive side heavier. Add more to it, and one day you will find that the side that was lighter has become heavier."

—*Swami Niranjanananda Saraswati*

Review of the Day
The practice of review of the day allows you to discover the triggers of krodha. The first stage is to see the external events and circumstances where you get angry. Once these circumstantial factors are identified, small adjustments in routine and lifestyle can be made that will help create a more balanced environment and space for interaction. The second stage is to realize the attitude, perceptions, assumptions and mode of thinking that cause the vritti. These mental patterns are the substantial cause of krodha, and ultimately these have to change. Developing understanding of what and how to change is the foundation of jnana yoga. Every evening before you go to bed review the day.

Stage 1: Identification of sensory triggers
1. Like watching a movie, view the events, situations and interactions during the day in reverse. From the present, go back in time and see yourself acting and reacting in different scenes throughout the day until you reach the time you woke up.
2. Notice the situations when you experienced krodha.

3. Identify the trigger. What happened to make you angry?
4. From which sense organ and sensory channel of information did the reaction of krodha come?
5. Were you able to restrain the activity of that sense? Did you identify with and pay more attention to it?
6. Are you able to isolate the feeling of dwesha that came from the senses and sense information? What was the cause of dwesha?
7. How did dwesha influence the mind? Were you able to restrain that mood and retain balance or did it take over the mind and behaviour?
8. How did you express and experience krodha?
9. What was the contribution of krodha to the situation? Was it constructive or destructive?
10. Visualize yourself being able to react differently if you experience the same situation again.

Anger, like fever, is a symptom which shows that something has gone wrong in the inner mechanism. The mental machinery gets heated for want of timely lubrication. The most effective of all lubricants is introspection or reflection. Even the most angry man realizes his folly after his anger is spent out. It is then that he begins to reflect upon what he did. If this reflection had come to him before he got angry, he would not have got angry at all. But that would be possible only if he had made reflection or introspection over his habit. The habit must be formed in good time if the evil is to be averted.

—*Swami Sivananda Saraswati*

Stage 2: Identification of internal triggers
1. Like watching a movie, view the events, situations and interactions during the day in reverse. From the present, go back in time and see yourself acting and reacting in different scenes throughout the day until you reach the time you woke up.

2. Notice the situations when you experienced krodha.
3. Identify the trigger. What happened to make you angry?
4. Identify the point where krodha started inside, the thought, feeling, or emotion. This may or may not be linked to an external event, but the focus is the internal reaction. Irritation, frustration, disappointment, a feeling of being slighted or offended, hurt pride, any of these.
5. Review the pattern of thinking that follows from that internal trigger.
6. Observe any memories of similar past events that you recalled at the time.
7. Identify the predominant characteristic of the thinking pattern, was it the frustration of desire, emotions of past memories, emotional based reasoning, subjective judgements of other people, generalization, prejudice or bias.
8. Notice how this pattern of feeling made you feel.
9. How did you express and experience krodha?
10. What was the contribution of krodha to the situation? Was it constructive or destructive?
11. Visualize yourself being able to react differently if you experience the same situation again.

Anger indicates a dissatisfied condition of the mind. In the state of dissatisfaction, there is a craving to eradicate that state and to be satisfied. When you are not able to satisfy yourself for whatever reason, anger manifests. Anger is the state of being dissatisfied. If you analyze the moments of anger which you express from time to time, in different situations, in different circumstances, in different conditions, you will notice that the primary cause of anger is dissatisfaction. This has been stated in the *Bhagavad Gita*. When the mind is not satisfied, anger arises, and anger becomes the force, the power to fill the vacuum that is felt by the mind.

—*Swami Niranjanananda Saraswati*

Pratipaksha bhavana

Find out the real cause of your anger and try to eradicate
it. If a man abuses you and calls you names, you become
furious at once. Your blood becomes hot. Why do you
feel offended when he calls you 'a dog' or 'a donkey'?
Have you developed now four legs and a tail like a dog?
Why do you get excited for little things? Enquire: What
is this abuse? Is it not mere vibration in the ether? Am I
body or Atman? No one can injure Atman. The Atman
of the abuser and the abused is one. Do I really gain
anything by retaliating? I waste my energy. I hurt the
feeling of another man. I disturb and pollute the thought
world. I do real harm to the world by sending a current
of hatred. This world is unreal. I will live here for a
short time only. Let me bear this insult. Let me excuse
him. I will develop inner mental strength and power of
endurance. You can thus very effectively eradicate the
feelings of anger. A time will come when you will not be
irritated even a bit by harsh words, abuses and insults of
this kind. You will not pay the least heed if a man says
that such and such a man has said bad words against
you. You will simply laugh the whole matter away. An
irritable man is very weak and has no mental strength.

—*Swami Sivananda Saraswati*

Pratipaksha bhavana means cultivation of the opposite quality.
Pratipaksha bhavana involves recognizing the moments
when the influence of the six conditions is highlighted
in the mind and learning how to generate the opposite
positive influence. Rather than allowing krodha to take over,
counteract it by focusing on the opposite positive quality.
Whenever the negative pattern of thought comes to the
mind, cultivate the opposite. When the feeling of anger and
frustration comes up, rather than fighting with the mind and
trying to suppress that reaction, develop the opposite quality
and focus on that.

Pratipaksha bhavana is especially important in managing of krodha due to the speed and intensity of the physiological response. The neuronal surge that activates the instinctive programming of the brain and body lasts for a very short period of time. If you can create even a few seconds delay before the vritti takes over, the prefrontal cortex has time to overcome the reaction of the amygdala. Once the prefrontal cortex is engaged, from the neuronal and physiological perspective, it is easier to control or bypass the reaction of krodha.

The first thing required is awareness and identification of krodha in whatever form; irritation, dissatisfaction, frustration, criticism, resentment, whatever comes up first on the mental screen. As soon as this appears, take the decision to create a different pattern in the mind. Change the vritti by introducing the opposite quality. When the feeling of krodha comes up, rather than struggling to restrain that reaction, develop the opposite quality and focus on that. If you feel irritation or frustration, focus on patience or serenity. Develop the experience of balance. If there is a defensive, volatile response to another person, perhaps something is said that offends or hurts, practise kshama and bring to mind the feeling and experience of forgiveness.

In this technique, pratipaksha bhavana is not about removing the negative, it is about ignoring the negative and cultivating the positive. By focusing on that quality, a different part of the brain is engaged. Pratipaksha bhavana opens access to the prefrontal cortex, facilitating the neuronal pathways related to reason, understanding, deliberation and contemplation on the consequences of actions. This reduces the intensity of the negative emotion and allows for reflection.

Pratipaksha bhavana also diverts the mental energy away from the vritti and towards a positive experience. The mind is fuelled by prana, chitta shakti. Maintaining the intensity of thought and emotion involved in vrittis like krodha requires a constant supply of prana, which is limited. Introducing a different cognitive focus diverts the prana from krodha to something else. This reduces the amount of prana engaged in krodha and the intensity of the vritti diminishes.

Pratipaksha bhavana is the first response, and once the window is open, you can use the understanding gained from the practice of SWAN and Review of the Day. Analyze, isolate the cause, and identify the influence of rajas or tamas on the mind. Without getting caught up in the experience, observe what is happening and focus on the opposite positive quality to dilute and diffuse the influence of rajas and tamas. By focusing on the positive you are highlighting the qualities that connect you with sattwa. This connection with sattwa helps divert and modify the tamasic and rajasic expressions of krodha.

There are different ways to practise pratipaksha bhavana. One way is the natural spontaneous method where you bring the opposite quality to the front of the mind whenever the reaction of krodha comes up. Another method utilizes the pratipaksha bhavana within a simple technique of antar mouna. This can be done every evening, before or after japa. Both can be practised together and they are complementary. Your success when confronted with the different situations and interactions throughout the day will directly influence the progress you make with the meditative technique.

> Meditate in the morning on the virtue of patience for ten minutes. Reflect and repeat the formula Om Patience mentally several times daily. Remember the saints and their lives. Say unto yourself, "I am patient now. I will never get irritated from today. I will manifest the virtue of patience in my daily life. I am getting better and better." Feel that you possess a magazine of patience. Think of the advantages of possessing this virtue and the disadvantages of irritability. You may fail many times but you will develop patience gradually and become an embodiment of patience.
>
> —*Swami Sivananda Saraswati*

TECHNIQUE

Stage 1: Preparation

Sit in a comfortable meditation posture, preferably siddhasana or padmasana. Adjust your position so that you do not have to move any part of the body during the practice. Make sure the spine is erect. Head, neck and shoulders should be slightly back. Place your hands on the knees in chin or jnana mudra. Close your eyes. Become aware of the breath and observe the flow of the natural breath.

Stage 2: Body posture

Switch your awareness to the body. Concentrate on your meditation posture. Feel your spine rising straight up from the floor, supporting the head. Be aware of the synchronized and balanced position of the arms and legs. Total awareness of the body.

Stage 3: Visualization of body

Visualize your body externally as if you were seeing it in a full-length mirror. See your body in the meditation posture from the front, from the back, from the right side, from the left side, from the top. See your body from all sides at one time. Intensify your awareness of the body. Maintain full awareness.

Stage 4: Steadiness and stillness

Be aware of your physical body, of your meditation posture and of nothing else. There should be total uninterrupted awareness of the whole body. The body is perfectly steady and motionless. Develop the feeling of steadiness.

Stage 5: Awareness of senses and sensory input

Become aware of the external sensorial experiences and information. Become aware of the ears, the sensory organ of the ears, and observe the information conveyed to the mind by the ears in the form of different sounds. Observe all the external sounds that you can hear. Observe with total awareness the experience of sound.

Stage 6: Awareness of thoughts

Move the awareness to the mind and the content of the mind. Become aware of thoughts arising inside the mind. Thoughts are manifestations or expressions of your inner self. Observe the spontaneous thinking process. Objective awareness. Become a witness of every thought that is going through the mind.

Stage 7: Awareness of krodha

Bring to mind an experience of krodha, a past memory when you have reacted in anger. Become aware of that expression of krodha and discover how it came into the mind. What was the trigger? What was the underlying mood or feeling of the mind at that time? Analyze it objectively. Which guna was predominating, tamas or rajas?

Stage 8: Underlying cause

Using the awareness of the gunas, try to locate the underlying cause. What is fuelling the experience of krodha? What is the particular perception that you have about yourself underneath the experience of anger? Identify the underlying cause.

Stage 9: Pratipaksha bhavana

Create the feeling and experience of the opposite quality. The positive quality will help you to remove the cause of krodha, and neutralize the reaction in the mind. Enhance the experience of the opposite quality, and allow that feeling to expand. Feel the positive quality permeating the mind and emotions.

Stage 10: Visualization

Visualize the same situation where you reacted with krodha, but this time it is the positive quality that guides your actions and responses to the situation. See yourself acting differently and expressing the positive.

Stage 11: Ending the practice

Become aware of the breath. Watch the breath as it flows in and out. Gradually become aware of the physical body, of the meditation posture. Feel the weight of the body against the floor. Be aware of the hands resting on the knees. Be aware of the whole physical body. Get ready to end the practice. Take a deep breath in and chant *Om* three times.

Applying pratipaksha bhavana has to be done with the right understanding: with dispassion, detachment and discrimination, *viveka* and *vairagya*. They develop the sattwic nature, which expresses itself not in the form of self-rebuke and guilt, but in the form of encouragement.

Pratipaksha bhavana is recognizing those moments, thoughts, flashes and expressions that cause disturbance in life and lead you towards suffering and replacing those flashes, moments, ideas, thoughts with positive, virtuous thoughts, ideas and acts that will bring contentment and joy. Make the effort to create the opposite of the negativity you are experiencing at present.

—*Swami Niranjanananda Saraswati*

7

Restraining Krodha with Hatha Yoga

Hatha yoga is practised in order to initiate a process in this physical body whereby the pranic molecules and the mental forces, which interact with each other in the scheme of life and existence, may be transformed. Unless the physical molecules are transformed, it is no use to discuss compassion or unity.

—*Swami Satyananda Saraswati*

Jnana yoga facilitates observation, awareness and understanding of the reaction of krodha in relation to sensory input and the mental attitudes and thinking patterns. You learn how and why you get angry. By using pratipaksha bhavana you create a different circuit in the brain and mind that can bypass the instinctive reaction of krodha and allow for reasoning, logic and appropriate decision-making.

Hatha yoga practices help to restrain and control the reaction of krodha by activating the frontal cortex of the brain, and diffusing the chemical and physiological reactions of the instinctive anger response. Excessive krodha creates imbalance in the physiological and pranic systems. This imbalance can be restrained and rectified using the appropriate hatha yoga practices.

Two areas in the brain are important, the amygdala which is in the limbic system and the prefrontal cortex in front of the brain, behind the forehead and above the eyes. The amygdala is like the on-switch for krodha, and the prefrontal cortex is the off-switch. The prefrontal cortex relates to the ability to maintain and control emotional states, anticipate consequences of actions, and rationalize. If this area of the brain is bypassed or unable to function properly, it will be very difficult, if not impossible to restrain the physiological effects of krodha.

The hatha yoga practices given below stimulate the prefrontal cortex area of the brain, rebalance the flow of neurotransmitters and help to harmonize the brain chemistry. The major sensory organs as well as the nadis connecting the brain and senses are stimulated and purified. The body and mind are energized and able to manage and respond to sensory input in a positive, creative and constructive manner. For full descriptions of the techniques, refer to *Asana Pranayama Mudra Bandha* by Swami Satyananda Saraswati, Yoga Publications Trust, Munger, India. All yoga practices should be learnt under the guidance of an experienced teacher and due regard should be given to the contra-indications for each practice. Slow, steady and systematic practice gives the most sustainable results.

SHATKARMAS

The spade work which we have to do in order to make yama and niyama the natural expression of our being, is the practice of hatha yoga. Purification of the 72,000 nadis which carry the computerized impulses throughout the body, and the six hatha yoga body purification techniques create a psychobiological harmony, and this harmony ultimately creates spontaneity of the positive dharma in us.

I am peaceful within and without, not because I am forcing myself to be, but on account of the great transformation that has taken place in the structure of my psychobiological system. It has become my nature to be non-violent and full of love and understanding.

—*Swami Satyananda Saraswati*

The *shatkarma* or six practices of purification in hatha yoga detoxify the physical body and rectify imbalances occurring due to stress and improper lifestyle. Cleaning the body internally is as important as cleaning the body externally. How would you feel if you did not clean your mouth or brush your teeth for one week? Internal purity of the body is necessary in order to experience harmony and balance. Cleansing the body will directly affect the mind. If the internal body is unclean disharmony will be experienced in the mind and this will manifest in the expression of the six conditions.

Jala neti (nasal cleansing with water)
Jala neti removes mucus and pollution from the nasal passages and sinuses, allowing air to flow without obstruction. A balance is brought about between the right and left nostrils and the corresponding left and right brain hemispheres, inducing a state of harmony and balance throughout the body and mind. This cleansing stimulates the frontal area of the brain, and has a calming influence.
Frequency: Once a week.

Kunjal (practice of vomiting water)

The practice of kunjal helps to rectify internal imbalances caused by overindulgence and release pent-up emotions and emotional blocks.

Frequency: Once every two weeks.

Laghoo shankhaprakshalana (short intestinal wash)

Laghoo shankhaprakshalana strengthens the immune system, reduces excessive mucus and purifies the blood. Shankhaprakshalana recharges the entire pranic body, purifies the nadis and restores the harmony of the five pranas. The pranic activation and balance of the right and left hemispheres of the brain purifies and rectifies chemical imbalance. Activation and balance of brain hemispheres encourages mental harmony and peace. The impact of sensory information upon the brain and mind is minimized and an automatic state of pratyahara is induced.

Frequency: Once a month

In order to purify the mind, it is necessary for the body as a whole to undergo a process of absolute purification. Hatha yoga is also known as the science of purification, not one type of purification, but six types. If you take an enema, this is one type of purification; shankhaprakshalana is another. Purification of the whole nervous system is also a part of hatha yoga. Besides purifying the physical body, we have to purify the nadis. The body has to be cleansed in six different ways for six different impurities. When you clear the body of these impurities, the nadis function and the energy blocks are released. Then the energies move like wave frequencies along the physical structure of the channel, and they go right up to the brain.

—*Swami Satyananda Saraswati*

ASANA

The easiest way to control anger is to practise shashank-asana. This practice controls the adrenaline and then the aggression and anger vanish. Anyone who gets angry should do this asana at night and then go to sleep immediately afterwards.

—Swami Niranjanananda Saraswati

Regular practice of asana is of great benefit in the restraint of the reaction of krodha. Asana corrects any imbalance in the relationship between the sympathetic and parasympathetic nervous systems and the incorrect hormonal distribution in the body. The endocrine system is regulated, and the production of adrenaline, noradrenaline and acetylcholine is restrained. The internal organs are massaged through the alternate movements of extension and compression, and hormones secreted in extreme reactions are flushed out. Regulation of the nervous system influences the pranic body and the twin flows of ida and pingala are also brought into harmony. This in turn calms the mental faculties.

One should never become involved with jealousy or anger, but if necessary the practice of *shashankasana*, the hare pose, will help. Shashankasana helps to control the adrenal glands and calms the mind. Practising shashank-asana daily soon brings about a total change in the nature of one's physiological behaviour. In shashankasana, what do you do? You bend forward and there is tension or stimulus created in the adrenal glands and they secrete a little more or a little less adrenalin according to the requirement of the system. When the adrenalin is injected and absorbed by the system, then the chemistry in the body changes and the behaviour of the sympathetic and parasympathetic nervous system also changes.

—Swami Satyananda Saraswati

97

PRANAYAMA

Prana entwines the mind like a creeper. Pranayama leads to the control of mind. Pranayama will put a break on the impulse of speech. It gives one an abundance of energy to check anger.

—*Swami Sivananda Saraswati*

Krodha is fuelled by prana. Anger is a hot and fiery reaction that is felt in both body and mind. The heat of krodha comes from prana. The more agitated and extreme the reaction, the more prana is directed into the vritti as fuel. Explosive outbursts deplete prana and have a detrimental effect upon the overall vitality of body and resilience of mind. If sustained this depletion of prana causes a fundamental imbalance in the pancha pranas and also impairs the ability of the mind to experience higher states of consciousness.

Pranayama techniques are used to cool the physical and mental systems, restrain the effects of krodha and divert awareness from stressors to relaxation. Cooling pranayamas like sheetali and sheetkari can be used, while heating pranayamas should be avoided. One simple method to restrain the instinctive physiological reaction of krodha and regain control of yourself is simple breath awareness. This can be practised anywhere at any time. Become aware of your breath. When you feel irritated, use abdominal breathing. Do not allow the breathing process to move upwards into the chest and thoracic regions, as this exacerbates the krodha response. If that does not help, focus on extending your exhalation. Exhale slowly for at least twice the duration of your inhalation. Before venting your frustration upon others, take ten long, slow, deep breaths and allow the physiological and pranic systems time to settle and realign. Then decide what is the appropriate course of action.

The sadhana to manage anger is pranayama. From the yogic perspective, anger is a nervous disorder and not a mental disorder. It is a disorder of the nerves, and nerves or nadis are the conductors and carriers of prana shakti. When you practise pranayama, especially nadi shodhana, the pranic flow is harmonized, and its effect impacts your mental behaviour. With the balancing of the nadis and the regulation of the prana flowing in them, the agitated mental behaviour can be brought under control. Those people who do get angry will notice a peculiar condition of breath in the moment of anger; the breath becomes shallow and fast. At that time, if you take deep breaths in and out and regulate your breathing pattern, you can manage your anger very efficiently and effectively.

—*Swami Niranjanananda Saraswati*

Bhramari pranayama (humming bee breath)

During the practice of bhramari pranayama a humming sound, like that of the bee, is produced with the exhaling breath. The whole pharynx, nasal cavities and sinuses become a resonating column. This sound produced in the vocal cords travels through the middle ear and into the internal ear. This humming sound causes the entire cerebral cortex to vibrate. The vibration has a soothing effect on the mind and nervous system. The environment of the whole body is controlled by the combined neuro-endocrinal systems. When the cerebral cortex is vibrating the harmonizing impulses are sent to the hypothalamus which has the capacity to control the pituitary gland. In this way, the endocrinal system is controlled and regulated. These impulses from the hypothalamus also affect the sympathetic nervous system which in turn affects all the internal systems of the body. The pineal gland which produces the hormone melatonin is also activated. Bhramari activates the frontal cortex of the brain, and relieves stress and cerebral tension.

In doing so it helps alleviate negative mental reactions, harmonize the mind and direct awareness inward.

Duration: Ten rounds or 2 to 5 minutes daily is sufficient.

Technique: Those who are comfortable with bhramari pranayama should practise with shanmukhi mudra.

Ujjayi (psychic breath)

Ujjayi is a tranquillizing pranayama which soothes the nervous system and calms the mind. It has a profoundly relaxing effect and induces a state of sensory withdrawal.

Duration: Begin with 20 breaths or one minute and slowly increase the practice up to 10 minutes.

> If people observe the breath and develop sound awareness for five minutes that will reduce cerebral and nervous tension. If there is too much pressure from work, then bhramari pranayama will stimulate melatonin which will reduce tension. People will feel more relaxed and peaceful, thanks to the release of melatonin.
>
> —*Swami Niranjanananda Saraswati*

Nadi shodhana (alternate nostril breathing)

The practice of nadi shodhana balances the two flows of prana, ida and pingala, which simultaneously regulates and harmonizes the activity of the nervous system and the brain hemispheres. It has a profoundly calming effect and relieves anxiety, improves concentration and stimulates the prefrontal cortex. This ratio establishes a calming rhythm for the brain and heart and is of maximum assistance in the management of krodha and other stress-related conditions.

Ratio: 1:2

Duration: 10 rounds or 10 to 15 minutes.

> With the practice of pranayama, more oxygen may be inhaled but that is not the important point. If oxygen alone is the purpose, then deep breathing would be sufficient. In pranayama inhalation and exhalation must

be practised in the ratio of 1:2, because this ratio is most beneficial for the heart. From the pulse you can observe that with inspiration the heart rate speeds up, whereas with expiration it slows down. Therefore, when the ratio of 1:2 is used, the overall effect is that of relaxation of the coronary muscles, but without a reduction of the supply of oxygen to the brain and body tissues.

—*Swami Satyananda Saraswati*

Sheetali (cooling breath)

Sheetali pranayama uses a powerful evaporative cooling mechanism during inhalation, delivering a gently cooling effect from the tongue and roof of the mouth, to the internal organs and deep tissues of the body. Sheetali affects the brain centres associated with instinctive responses and temperature regulation. It cools and reduces the mental agitation and emotional excitement associated with krodha. Excess heat in the physiological system is reduced and the functioning of internal organs is improved. Additionally the practice aids in the regulation of hunger and thirst, both of which are contributing factors in the reaction of krodha.

Duration: Begin with 10 rounds and gradually increase up to 5 minutes of practice.

Technique: Experienced practitioners can include antar kumbhaka.

Sheetkari (hissing breath)

As for sheetali.

Aggression can be combated by the practice of sheetali and sheetkari pranayama, but I think you should firstly make a thorough study of your personality.

—*Swami Satyananda Saraswati*

MUDRAS

Mudras influence the physical and pranic circuitry between the body and the brain. They channel and redirect the prana for optimum utility. The mudras that use the sense organs like eyes, tongue, ears, nose and hands purify and harmonize the pranic conduit between the senses and the brain, enabling better management of sensory information. Mudras using the eyes have a profound effect on the brain and directly influence the 30–40 percent of the cerebral cortex engaged in processing visual sensorial input. Also relevant in the management of krodha are the mudras that stimulate the orbital frontal lobe, the part of the brain directly over the left eye.

Shambhavi mudra (eyebrow centre gazing)

Shambhavi mudra uses the eyes, the sensory organs of sight, and has a profound effect on the brain and senses. Shambhavi redirects the sense of sight and the sensory prana from the lower centres of the brain to the frontal cortex area. This redirection of sensory input and prana purifies, stimulates and harmonizes frontal cortex activity, calms the mind, and removes emotional stress and anger. Shambhavi also activates the eye muscles and releases accumulated tension in this area.

Duration: Start with 3 rounds and gradually increase to 5 rounds over a period of months.

Nasikagra drishti (nose tip gazing)

At the physical level nasikagra drishti involves gazing at the nose tip creating a state of introspection and calm concentration. Nasikagra is an excellent technique in the restraint of krodha and helps to calm disturbed states of mind. The nose tip is associated with mooladhara chakra and the level of consciousness involved with instinctive responses to life. Activating mooladhara encourages a progression from insecurity and reaction towards a more balanced understanding of the individual in relationship to the external world.

Duration: Start with 30 seconds and gradually increase to maximum 5 minutes over a period of months.

Shanmukhi mudra (closing the seven gates)

Shanmukhi mudra involves redirecting the awareness inside by closing the six doors of outer perception: the two eyes, the two ears, the nose and the mouth. Neurological connectivity between the senses and the frontal cortex is increased and while the awareness is introverted both ida and pingala are stimulated. Through this practice, areas of the cortex are consciously brought into relationships which would otherwise not normally occur.

Duration: Start with 3 rounds and gradually increase to 5 rounds over a period of months.

Nasikagra drishti, nose tip gazing, calms anger and disturbed states of mind. The powers of concentration are developed. If performed with awareness for a long period, it helps to awaken mooladhara chakra and induce meditative states. Shambhavi mudra, gazing at the eyebrow centre, calms the mind, thus removing emotional stress and anger. Concentration, mental stability and the state of thoughtlessness are developed.

—*Swami Niranjanananda Saraswati*

DAILY PROGRAM

Asana

- Tadasana x 10
- Tiryak tadasana x 10
- Kati chakrasana x 10
- Surya namaskara x 5 to 10 rounds
- Shavasana
- Vipareeta karani asana x 1
- Dhanurasana x 3
- Simhagarjanasana x 5
- Shashankasana static 5 to 10 minutes
- Vajrasana static 3 to 5 minutes
- Paschimottanasana x 3
- Kashtha takshanasana x 10
- Naukasana x 5
- Shavasana, with abdominal breathing

Pranayama

- Nadi shodhana (1:2 ratio) x 10
- Bhramari x 10
- Sheetkari or sheetali 5 minutes
- Ujjayi 5 minutes

Mudra

- Nasikagra x 2 to 5 minutes
- Shanmukhi x 3 to 5 rounds
- Shambhavi x 3 to 5 rounds (held for 5 breaths)

Anger is one of the biggest barriers in life and jealousy is absolutely unnecessary and useless. Habitual anger means there is too much adrenalin in the system. The nervous system and glands react promptly to the various mental states.

When there is balance between sympathetic and parasympathetic nervous systems, there is calmness and tranquillity. So, in the science of hatha yoga, the body, mind, emotions, intellect and feelings are all interrelated. They are not considered as different from each other. Your mental problems, conflicts, psychosis, schizophrenia, anger, excessive passions, lack of memory, absence of coordination, exhaustion, guilt, or even lack of passion, may be due to a faulty system in the body.

—*Swami Satyananda Saraswati*

105

8

Managing Krodha through Raja Yoga

The formations on the superstructure of the mind are the tendencies of the mind which we experience in our day-to-day life. Anger and jealousy are not unholy. Passion and hatred are not sinful. These are the tendencies of the mind caused by external stimuli from the life which we face during our period of experience of *raga* and *dwesha* – like and dislike, attraction and repulsion, passion and anger. I assure you that we can never control these unless we go to the very base. The base is *chitta*, the mind, not the formations of the mind.

—*Swami Satyananda Saraswati*

Hatha yoga techniques help to restrain the physiological aspects of krodha, but management of the vritti takes place through the practice of raja yoga. There are two distinct ways that the vritti takes form and these are the currents of raga and dwesha. When krodha stems from dwesha, the trigger is sensorial input perceived as negative, threatening or insulting. When krodha stems from raga we are dealing with the aspect of kama, the realm of desire existing within the mind itself. The trigger for this type of krodha is the frustration of expectation, desire or attachment.

At the external level of senses and interaction with the world, management of krodha means working to reduce the reaction of dwesha in life. When the tendency towards dwesha reduces and the negativity of mind lessens, the vritti of krodha will naturally subside. At the internal level of mind and mental conditioning, management of krodha is reduction of attachment and desire in life. Therefore, the raja yoga sadhana begins by generating a balance between the experiences of raga and dwesha, so that the extremes of each reduce. The process of reducing the extremes of opposite reaction happens through relaxation.

Relaxation and yoga nidra
Relaxation is the first requirement. The practice of yoga nidra is a systematic process of physical and mental relaxation. Krodha is like an internal fire that is constantly heating and agitating the body and mind. Without methods to release this agitation, the effect cumulates. Over time, this results in physical and mental imbalance compounded by patterns of thought and reaction that are like throwing kerosene on the fire. During yoga nidra a process of physical and mental relaxation is initiated and the tensions of the body and mind are progressively released.

Following physical relaxation, the progression of mental relaxation begins when the mind is disconnected from sensorial activity and engagement. The twin currents of raga and dwesha are disconnected from the input of the senses and their influence on the mind subsides. The dwesha source of anger arising from external input is cut off. A mind that is constantly tense and under stress is more likely to perceive circumstances and people as threatening. When sensorial connections are withdrawn, the perception of threat is no longer imminent and the intensity diminishes. The deep grooves of reaction created in the mental field gradually recede and the influence of krodha on the mind lessens.

The sensory withdrawal in yoga nidra generates a deeper experience of relaxation in which mental dissipations reduce and awareness expands. When this happens a state of balance and equipoise is attained. The active awareness, now freed from the confines of sensory activity, spans the different levels of consciousness. It is here that the mind is able to turn inwards and release the impressions accumulated due to the reactions of raga and dwesha. The point is to maintain a state of mental equipoise in the experience of pleasure, as well as pain. In the state of yoga nidra both raga and dwesha are perceived and experienced equally. When the mind is able to experience both within a balanced field of mental energy, the power of raga and dwesha on the mind is nullified. When the intensity of reaction lessens, awareness increases and the mind can turn inwards.

Daily practice of yoga nidra with the appropriate sankalpa will allow the mind to release accumulated stress and offset the detrimental impact of krodha. More importantly, dedicated and regular practice of yoga nidra has the potential to restructure the mental conditioning, bringing about a stability and balance between the extremes of raga and dwesha. This is important in tackling krodha that is the result of frustrated desires and expectations. Here subterranean patterns of thought and modes of thinking that exacerbate krodha naturally and spontaneously come to the surface. Once revealed, they can be assessed objectively and dismantled.

Yoga says that the faculties and energies of the mind are dissipated at present like four wild horses running in all directions. If we cannot stop our mind or emotions, or control negative thoughts, how can we achieve a spiritual state? There is jealousy, anger, pride, and when we sit for meditation, we think, 'I am going to have darshan of God'. This is a futile hope. Until mental wellbeing is attained through the techniques of pratyahara, dharana and dhyana, we will not be able to control the other manifestations of our personality.

—*Swami Niranjanananda Saraswati*

Pratyahara

The next challenge is to create the same sense of mental and emotional balance whilst in the middle of sensorial activity and engagement. In the *Bhagavad Gita* (2.64) Sri Krishna explains that when the mind is under control it is possible to remain free from raga and dwesha even while using the objects of the senses:

रागद्वेषवियुक्तैस्तु विषयानिन्द्रियैश्चरन् ।
आत्मवश्यैर्विधेयात्मा प्रसादमधिगच्छति ॥

Raagadveshaviyuktaistu vishayaanindriyaishcharan;
Aatmavashyairvidheyaatmaa prasaadamadhigachchhati.

But the self-controlled man, moving among the objects with the senses restrained and free from attraction and repulsion, attains to peace.

The specific area of raja yoga that focuses on this interaction between the senses and the mind is pratyahara. *Pratyahara* is the term given in raja yoga to describe the approach, techniques and methods that allow the practitioner to disconnect or withdraw the mind from the influence of sensorial inputs. Pratyahara involves reversing the flow of awareness from the outgoing movement that entangles the mind with the world, to an inward movement that allows the mind to focus within, to discover its true nature.

In order to reverse a flow, the first thing that has to happen is restraint of the existing motion. In order to change the course of a river, a dam is created. Once the flow is restrained, the water can be diverted easily to another course. Simply trying to restrain the water without providing for an alternate route is not going to work. Eventually there will be an overflow. The same happens in the mind. To manage the interaction of mind and senses you need restraint, withdrawal and diversion. Two techniques are given by Swami Niranjanananda for this level of mind management: the yama of danti and the niyama of indriya nigraha. To control the mind is extremely difficult for beginners and if the senses run riot, it is practically impossible. For this reason, indriya nigraha comes first because the mind is led by the senses.

> The theory or doctrine that the mind should be controlled first is quite correct. This practice is intended for the first-class type of aspirants. The middling type of aspirants should control the senses first. The senses always have an outgoing tendency. The mind operates through the senses. Control of one goes hand in hand with control of the others. Control of the senses is also control of the mind, because the mind is a bundle of senses only, there is no mind without the senses.
>
> —*Swami Sivananda Saraswati*

Indriya nigraha

Indriya nigraha works at the area of interaction between the senses and mind. The senses are always externalized, they are constantly flowing outwards, keeping you connected to the external world. The mind receives sensory information constantly, twenty-four hours a day. Most people are unaware of the majority of sensorial input, because the awareness is limited. It is only when the raga or dwesha reaction is prominent, that there is a corresponding reaction in the mind. In the management of krodha, it is not only the actual sensory contact that has to be restrained and managed, but also the raga or dwesha component.

The first step is to create a balance between raga and dwesha. If dwesha predominates, if you generally react negatively to the world around you, then develop awareness of the positive. Expand the awareness of the positive influence of sensorial information. This shifts the sensorial engagement from tamas to sattwa. When sattwa predominates, the senses are naturally restrained and the information coming from their engagement with the material world creates joy, peace and harmony. When glimpses of the beauty of life shine through the clouds of material existence, identify the cause and endeavour to repeat and expand that experience.

Identify those things that trigger the experience of happiness, contentment, peace and balance within. Use the senses to take the mind in the right direction. Instead of regular exposure to television and internet, supplying a daily intake of drama, aggression and hostility to the senses, unplug and go for a walk in nature. Listen to mantra. Practise mouna. Working with indriya nigraha in daily life means making small adjustments to ensure that the external conditions are optimal. Choose the sattwic options of sensorial activity. Tamasic and rajasic activity will pull you downwards, while sattwa is always uplifting. Tamas and rajas lead to further bondage and entanglement with the material dimension, but sattwa helps you to identify and connect with the spiritual dimension.

When sensory information is interpreted as a threat or otherwise causes the reaction of dwesha, the first thing you need to apply is restraint. It is the reaction of dwesha that has to be curtailed and restrained, before krodha kicks in. It may be a very subtle reaction of dwesha, hardly perceptible, or it may be a huge spike in the consciousness. Do not allow this reaction to increase and gain momentum. Hold the mind steady. The neurological response to krodha lasts for less than two seconds. It is in those two seconds that you need to restrain the spike of mental energy before the vritti can establish itself.

The second stage is withdrawal of the dwesha component. Do not let dwesha become the predominant response of the mind to sensorial input. Be alert, aware and determined to practise indriya nigraha in daily life and interactions. How easy or how difficult it is, will be determined by the extremity of the reaction. If dwesha is extreme, it will be much more difficult to withdraw and disconnect that reaction from the sense input. When dwesha is intense, the sensory input can repeat itself in the mind indefinitely, like a feedback loop. The potential threat will be alive in the mind and the vritti of krodha will continuously ignite from this potential.

> Introspect. Look within. Watch the gunas carefully. Be vigilant. Stand as a doorkeeper. Allow only sattwic thoughts to pass through the door of the mental factory. Check rajas. Curb tamas. Convert tamas into rajas and rajas into sattwa.
>
> —*Swami Sivananda Saraswati*

The three gunas will also influence the activity of the senses and the mental association and perceptions. Under the influence of tamas, the senses are dull and the mind when associating with them is prone to dwesha and erroneous negative interpretations. *Pramada* or the condition of negligence, carelessness and heedlessness is characteristic of the tamasic sensorial engagement. Instinctive responses dominate and krodha is the outcome. When rajas prevails, the behaviour of the senses is characterized by *asama* or restlessness, desire and agitation. The senses will jump from one object to another seeking pleasure and stimulation. If this search for pleasure is frustrated, krodha takes form with lightning speed.

If there is an inclination towards a continual negative assessment, counteract and restrain this. Observe the negative commentary throughout the day and change the channel of constant criticism. It is not that you try to shut the senses off, just change the way you interpret the information. Criticism is a negative response born of tamas and it takes away the beauty of life. Appreciation, delight, wonder, awe, veneration and regard are all responses of the mind that can be cultivated to pull you out of tamas and connect with sattwa.

The senses are the avenues of sense-knowledge. They are the gateways of perception for the self. When light shines in all the gates of the body, such as the eyes, ears then knowledge arises. The ears shun what is improper to be heard. The eyes abandon what they should not look at. The tongue avoids to speak anything that is not right to speak of. The mind is not attracted by the sensual objects. Purity thus increases gradually by restraint.

—*Swami Sivananda Saraswati*

After restraint comes diversion, the techniques that propel the awareness in a different direction, away from the dwesha response and towards something positive. Focusing on a negative emotion like krodha will intensify the experience. However, distracting the mind from that vritti will lessen the intensity, because the brain has limited resources. Deliberately choosing to think about something else means that there is less prana to feed the vritti of krodha.

Research suggests this is because both cognitive tasks and emotional responses make use of the same limited mental resources. Mental resources used to perform a cognitive task are no longer available for emotional processes. Accordingly, you can pull the prana out of the cycle of negative emotion by engaging in a cognitive activity, such as counting to ten or doing math equations. Other tools that can be used to divert the awareness at that time are: deep abdominal breathing, counting to ten, drinking cold water, maintaining silence until the reaction passes, mental japa of the mantra *Om*, remembering someone you love and revere, or visualizing your ishta devata or guru. The diversion you create in the mind is a movement away from tamasic and rajasic conditioning towards the experience of sattwa.

The process of indriya nigraha through restraint, withdrawal and diversion reflects the process of the transformation of the senses. The negativity of tamas is curtailed through restraint. The volatility and dynamism of rajas is withdrawn before it can inflame that negativity, and finally the senses are diverted towards sattwa. When sattwa pre-

113

dominates, the senses are purified. They do not run towards external objects. The understanding is not clouded and the mental response to sensorial input is one of knowledge and illumination. Clear vision, understanding and happiness are the outcome of the sattwic interaction of senses and mind. When happiness, wisdom and illumination increase and appropriate action becomes a spontaneous expression in life, then the senses are under the influence of sattwa. This transformation is possible through indriya nigraha.

If you find it difficult to control anger, leave the place at once and take a brisk walk. Drink some cold water immediately. This cools down the body and mind. Chant *Om* loudly like a lion for ten minutes and then chant *Om Shanti* mentally or verbally for five minutes.

Think of the picture of your ishta. Pray. Repeat your ishta mantra for ten minutes. Gradually the anger will vanish.

—*Swami Sivananda Saraswati*

TECHNIQUE

Stage 1: Preparation
Sit in a comfortable meditation posture, preferably siddhasana/siddha yoni asana or padmasana. Adjust your position so that you do not have to move any part of the body during the practice. Make sure the spine is erect. Head, neck and shoulders should be slightly back. Place your hands on the knees in chin or jnana mudra. Close your eyes. Become aware of the breath and observe the flow of the natural breath.

Stage 2: Body posture
Switch your awareness to the body. Concentrate on your meditation posture. Feel your spine rising straight up from the floor, supporting the head. Be aware of the synchronized and balanced position of the arms and legs. Total awareness of the body.

Stage 3: Visualization of body

Visualize your body externally as if you were seeing it in a full-length mirror. See your body in the meditation posture from the front, from the back, from the right side, from the left side, from the top. See your body from all sides at one time. Intensify your awareness of the body. Maintain full awareness.

Stage 4: Steadiness and stillness

Be aware of your physical body, of your meditation posture and of nothing else. There should be total uninterrupted awareness of the whole body. The body is perfectly steady and motionless. Develop the feeling of steadiness.

Stage 5: Immobility of the body

Make a resolve, "I will not move my body throughout the whole practice. I will remain steady and motionless like a statue." Even if you feel an impulse to move, try to overcome this urge. Say to yourself, "I will not move any part of my body until the end of the practice."

Stage 6: Awareness of senses and sensory input

Become aware of the external sensorial experiences and information. Become aware of the ears, the sensory organ of the ears, and observe the information conveyed to the mind by the ears in the form of different sounds. Observe all the external sounds that you can hear. Observe with total awareness the experience of sound.

Become aware of the skin of the body. Observe the different sensations of touch, the feeling of clothing against the skin, feeling of the feet, legs, thighs touching the floor, feeling of air upon the skin. Awareness of the total sensorial input conveyed to the mind through the skin.

Become aware of the nose and the nostrils. Observe the flow of breath travelling through the nostrils. Sensorial input passes to the mind via the sense of smell. Maintain total external awareness of the sense of smell. What are the smells coming within the range of the senses?

Become aware of the mouth. Observe the tongue, the sense organ of taste. Observe and notice if there are any taste sensations within the field of your awareness.

Stage 7: Developing drashta bhava

Expand the awareness and become aware of the entire process of sensory involvement. This process is threefold. The first is the sense organ, the second is the object of experience, and the third is yourself, who is the spectator, the witness of this process.

Develop this threefold awareness. Awareness of the sense organ experiencing, the object of experience and yourself as the observer.

First is the ears, the sense organ, and the second is the sounds, the object of experience. You are the witness, observing these. The subject and the object, the ears and the sound, the eyes and the form, the skin and the touch, the tongue and the taste, the nose and the smell. You are the witness, experience *drashta bhava*, develop the attitude of a witness.

Stage 8: Awareness of raga and dwesha

Maintain the introversion of your sense experiences, and observe the reaction to the sense input in the mind. Become aware of the different sounds registering in the field of your awareness. Isolate any reaction of like or dislike, pleasure or displeasure. Withdraw the mind from that reaction. The sense experiences came from outside, but the raga and dwesha is arising inside the mind. The sound is outside, but the feeling of like or dislike is inside. You can withdraw the senses from the feeling of like or dislike. Disconnect the inside and the outside experience.

Become aware of the skin of the body. Become aware of the different sensations of touch registering in the field of your awareness. Isolate any reaction of like or dislike, pleasure or displeasure and withdraw the mind from that reaction. The sensation is outside, but the feeling of like or dislike is inside. You can withdraw the senses from the

116

feeling of like or dislike. Disconnect the inside and the outside experience.

Become aware of the nose and the nostrils. Observe the flow of breath travelling through the nostrils conveying information to the mind via the sense of smell. Is there any sensorial input from the nose registering in the field of your awareness? Isolate any reaction of like or dislike, pleasure or displeasure, and disconnect the senses from that reaction. Withdraw the experience of raga and dwesha from the senses.

Become aware of the tongue, the sense organ of taste. Are there any taste sensations presently within the field of your awareness? Notice any feeling of like or dislike and then withdraw the senses from that reaction. You can withdraw the senses from the feeling of like or dislike. Disconnect the inside and the outside experience.

Stage 9: Simultaneous awareness

Become aware of all five senses, and the sensorial input, the information coming from the senses. Observe these one by one. This is the peripheral area of interaction between the internal and the outside world. You are the observer of both the external experiences and the internal experiences and the information conduit made by the senses. Develop this experience.

Stage 10: Ending the practice

Become aware of the breath. Watch the breath as it flows in and out. Gradually become aware of the physical body, of the meditation posture. Feel the weight of the body against the floor. Be aware of the hands resting on the knees. Be aware of the whole physical body. Get ready to end the practice. Take a deep breath in and chant *Om* three times.

Danti

Indriya nigraha works at the sensorial level, to restrain dwesha and help you to regain control before krodha takes over. Once krodha is established, indriya nigraha will not help, because the vritti is not reliant upon the senses. Although sensory input may have been the trigger, in this scenario krodha is fuelled by the content and processes of the mind. Danti helps you manage krodha that is related to the frustration of kama, rather than sensorial reaction. The assumptions, expectations and judgements that operate the mental conditioning and the stored content, impressions and memories are the area of focus. This is why the practice of danti is more difficult, because the problem and the process of counteracting krodha at that level are purely internal and relates to mental conditioning. Danti is a tool of mind management to be used in daily life, and also as a pratyahara technique.

> Generally, one thinks about the anger only after one has expressed it. Very few people think while they are angry. If you reflect upon the nature of your anger and analyze the cause of the reaction, then continued performance of this awareness will eventually develop the time span of awareness, and then even at the time of feeling angry you will be aware of that anger and be able to alter it.
>
> —*Swami Niranjanananda Saraswati*

Danti in daily life

The first step is awareness, observation of what is happening in the mind. If you are able to observe the memories and patterns of thought interacting with the vritti of krodha, then there is also the possibility to restrain that interaction. What you observe is the vritti of krodha interacting with specific patterns of thought, which are tamasic and negative, or accessing the field of memory and stored experience. These are all the data files in the hard drive that constantly influence mental conditioning and trigger different reactions and attitudes of mind.

The vritti of krodha has a specific vibration and range of influence that attracts thoughts and memories of similar vibratory quality. When krodha is active, the memories that come to the surface easily will not be the positive ones, they will evoke the same feelings of aggression, frustration and resentment. Similarly, the thought patterns catalyzed by krodha, the way of thinking about people and situations will not be positive, optimistic and friendly. The thoughts will be based on emotionally subjective criticism and the perceptions and judgements are likely to be erroneous.

When anger assumes a grave form, it becomes difficult to control. It should therefore, be controlled even when it is in the form of a small ripple in the subconscious mind, *chitta*. One should watch the mind very, very cautiously. Whenever there is the least symptom or indication of light irritability, then and there it must be nipped. Then it becomes very easy to control anger. Be careful and vigilant and watch the ripple, then only you are a sage.

—*Swami Sivananda Saraswati*

It is here that danti comes in to close the floodgates before the influence of krodha sweeps all the positivity from the mind. The mind has to be restrained and held in check. Do not indulge in the mental pattern of congruence between krodha and the memories of past negative experiences. Do not allow the congruence of mood to evoke the full range of negative past experiences. Curtail that and neutralize their effect and influence. If a particular memory or thought pattern becomes dominant, the next step is to withdraw the mind from that impression. This cuts the link between krodha and the content of the mind.

The link between these two needs to be withdrawn. Sometimes this will be comparatively easy, and other times it will be more difficult, depending on the intensity.

The heavier the impression, the stronger the force of the vritti that develops in the mind. Repeated practice will help to lighten the load of past impressions and negative conditioning to reveal the latent potentials and inner effulgence of the mind. The final step is diversion of the mind to a positive experience or a different task. Mental energy is limited and a powerful vritti like krodha requires a lot of prana. When you occupy the mind with something else, the chitta shakti, the subtle prana of the mind, is diverted to that activity and the supply to the vritti decreases.

Suppressed anger is the worst form of anger because it means restriction of emotional expression. People who cannot express emotions have psychological hang-ups of one type or another. That psychological hang-up becomes their personality, their nature, their attitude. The solution is to witness the suppressed anger in meditation. Mantra helps to bring out the suppressed anger. Once you are able to bring to the surface of your mind the reason for your unhappiness, and you have enough mental clarity to work to improve that reason, you will find a change in the intensity of the aggression and anger.

—*Swami Niranjanananda Saraswati*

TECHNIQUE

Stage I: Preparation
Sit in a comfortable meditation posture, preferably siddhasana/siddha yoni asana or padmasana. Adjust your position so that you do not have to move any part of the body during the practice. Make sure the spine is erect. Head, neck and shoulders should be slightly back. Place your hands on the knees in chin or jnana mudra. Close your eyes. Become aware of the breath and observe the flow of the natural breath.

Stage 2: Body posture

Switch your awareness to the body. Concentrate on your meditation posture. Feel your spine rising straight up from the floor, supporting the head. Be aware of the synchronized and balanced position of the arms and legs. Total awareness of the body.

Stage 3: Visualization of body

Visualize your body externally as if you were seeing it in a full-length mirror. See your body in the meditation posture from the front, from the back, from the right side, from the left side, from the top. See your body from all sides at one time. Intensify your awareness of the body. Maintain full awareness.

Stage 4: Steadiness and stillness

Be aware of your physical body, of your meditation posture and of nothing else. There should be total uninterrupted awareness of the whole body. The body is perfectly steady and motionless. Develop the feeling of steadiness.

Stage 5: Immobility of the body

Make a resolve, "I will not move my body throughout the whole practice. I will remain steady and motionless like a statue." Even if you feel an impulse to move, try to overcome this urge. Say to yourself, "I will not move any part of my body until the end of the practice."

Stage 6: Awareness of senses and sensory input

Become aware of the external sensorial experiences and information. Become aware of the ears, the sensory organ of the ears, and observe the information conveyed to the mind by the ears in the form of different sounds. Observe all the external sounds that you hear. Observe with total awareness the experience of sound. The sounds are conveyed to the mind through the ears.

Become aware of the skin of the body. Observe the different sensations of touch, the feeling of clothing against the skin, feeling of the feet, legs, thighs touching the floor, feeling of air upon the skin. Observe the sensations, the sensorial input from the skin coming within the field of awareness.

Become aware of the nose and the nostrils. Observe the flow of breath travelling through the nostrils. Maintain total external awareness of the sense of smell. Is there any sensorial input from the nose? What are the smells coming within the range of the senses?

Become aware of the mouth. Observe the tongue, the sense organ of taste. Observe and notice if there are any taste sensations within the field of your awareness.

Stage 7: Developing drashta bhava

Expand the awareness and become aware of the entire process of sensory involvement. This process is threefold. The first is the sense organ, the second is the object of experience, and the third is yourself, who is the spectator, the witness of this process.

Develop this threefold awareness. Awareness of the sense organ experiencing, the object of experience and yourself as the observer.

First is the ears, the sense organ, and the second is the sounds, the object of experience. You are the witness, observing these. The subject and the object, the ears and the sound, the eyes and the form, the skin and the touch, the tongue and the taste, the nose and the smell. You are the witness. Experience drashta bhava. Develop the attitude of a witness.

Stage 8: Awareness of thoughts

Move from this sensorial awareness to the mind and the content of the mind. Become aware of thoughts arising inside the mind. Thoughts are manifestations or expressions of your inner self. Observe the spontaneous thinking process. Become a witness of every thought that is going through the mind.

Stage 9: Identification of krodha

Select a past reaction of krodha and review that experience. Identify the cause of krodha. Is it the experience of dwesha, a negative reaction to an association, a situation, or person? Is it frustration of raga, attachment or desire? Observe the feelings associated with that experience. Become aware of the changes to your mood.

Stage 10: Identification of guna

Observe the nature and behaviour of the mind. Which guna is predominant? Is it tamasic or is it rajasic? Krodha linked to negativity and fear is related to tamas. Does the reaction of krodha reduce the feeling of being threatened and help you to feel secure? This is tamasic krodha. If krodha is a dynamic explosive feeling that comes because your desires have been frustrated, the guna influencing the mind is rajasic. Observe the operation of the gunas and their influence upon the mind.

Stage 11: Danti

Observe the influence of krodha through the impressions or memories that come to the surface of the mind. See the interaction and influence of krodha with different content of the mind, thoughts, thinking patterns, memories. Now withdraw the connection between krodha and memory, disconnect the present pattern of mind from the past event. Simply observe objectively and then withdraw the link between krodha and the content, the impressions of mind. Divert the awareness to a positive memory and allow the feeling of peace and calm to permeate the mind.

Stage 12: Ending the practice

Become aware of the breath. Watch the breath as it flows in and out. Gradually become aware of the physical body, of the meditation posture. Feel the weight of the body against the floor. Be aware of the hands resting on the knees. Be aware of the whole physical body. Get ready to end the practice. Take a deep breath in and chant *Om* three times.

Pratyahara does not stop with observing the thoughts and the surface activity of the mind. Dharana does not stop with the attainment of concentration and one-pointedness; that is the definition of the word dharana. Dhyana, meditation, does not begin by closing the eyes, but begins when you have subdued the six enemies of life. The journey begins when you overcome the six conditions that disturb the balance and peace of mind and life. The purpose of yoga sadhana is not the management of thoughts or even the management of emotions. You have to move towards the cause of the disturbance in relation to the six enemies that you confront every day.

—*Swami Niranjanananda Saraswati*

9

Transforming Krodha through Lifestyle Yama and Niyama

If you empty something from a pot, some other thing will fill the vacuum, even if it is only air. In the same manner, if you are removing kama you have to fill the space with something else: *santosha*, contentment. If you are lessening krodha, fill up with *shantata*, serenity. You have to see how the negative can be compensated with a positive attitude, idea and expression.

—*Swami Niranjanananda Saraswati*

SHANTATA

Shantata is the lifestyle yama given for the management of krodha. The word *shantata* describes the internal experience of mental and emotional balance or serenity that becomes a part of the external expression in life. Most people have experienced glimpses of shantata in life, but these are fleeting moments. That brief moment of peace, tranquillity, harmony and deep, abiding calm, when everything is equipoised is shantata. In those moments awareness is balanced between the inner and outer experience. This leads to equipoise and the feeling of serenity. Shantata is experience that comes from balanced awareness.

We often harbour the misconception that external circumstances are at fault for the lack of peace in our lives, and hope for the day when the situation will become conducive to the experience of serenity and peace of mind. Shantata is not dependent upon the external situation; it is the result of sustained effort to restrain and purify the senses, mind and emotions. Shantata is not something that is dependent upon external circumstances. It is an inner attainment. Generally, people try to change the circumstances, personalities and interactions of life, in order to experience peace. This only intensifies the externalization of awareness and the feeling of imbalance. Instead of thinking that it is the external circumstances – the job, colleagues, relationships, or money that has to change, we need to realize that the changes to make are inside. It is this internal adjustment and fine-tuning that brings about the balance of shantata.

From the yogic perspective, shantata exists inside each person as a quality inherent in the sattwic nature. This truth has been proclaimed by spiritual luminaries over the centuries; peace is your birthright, not anger, hostility and bitterness. From peace comes the experience of *ananda*, bliss. Bliss is your true nature, not unhappiness and suffering. Shantata begins when the mind is able to balance the internal and external involvement. Involvement, attachment and entanglement in the material dimension causes dissipation, imbalance and discord. To experience shantata, remove the causes of imbalance, agitation and stress in life. When these are removed, you will discover the peace and harmony that lies within, inherent in the pure expression of human nature.

Manage the external involvement

As long as the mind and senses are 100 percent externalized and engaged in the world, there is the dual experience of pain and pleasure, happiness and unhappiness. The mind swings constantly from raga to dwesha, expectation and attachment, to disappointment, frustration and suffering. This creates dissipation, and balance is lost. Externalization and dissipation creates spikes in the mental energy field. All of the six conditions, including krodha, are the spikes of mind and emotion that take you away from the experience of shantata. These spikes are so all consuming that the existence of shantata as a state of being is forgotten. A state of imbalance and constant agitation is the result.

Krodha is nothing but agitation in the mind and prana that floods the body with a cocktail of chemical imbalance. The removal of the influence of krodha begins with kshama and danti. The understanding of shantata evolves from the practice of these two yamas in a sequential progression. Kshama is used to remove the blockages of tamasic krodha and counter the spikes and claws of rajasic krodha. Danti is a process of restraint and redirection where the turbulence of aggression, resentment and hostility is calmed through reflection upon alternative mental patterns and the development of positive qualities. The tamasic and rajasic reactions of krodha are restrained. The externalized mind that was entangled in sensorial experience and reaction is redirected inwards.

The next state is moderation of these oscillations of mind and senses, through indriya nigraha and danti. These help you to regain balance. Shantata is a state of mind that is not disturbed by the senses or sensorial inputs. The balanced mind can receive and process the information from the senses, without fluctuation or disturbance. The mind that is externalized and looking outside to the material world for happiness, satisfaction and fulfilment is unable to do this. When there is agitation and constant striving to fulfil expectations and ambitions in life, krodha arises as an aggressive spike of frustration in the mind. This does not mean that shantata is the result of obtaining what you want. Shantata happens when you accept and flow with what is, trying to do your best in any circumstance or situation.

The attainment of inner purity is achieved when you have vanquished all six conditions. The purity and peace that is achieved is not an imposed idea. It is not something to strive for; rather, it is a natural outcome of you having managed your six enemies. With this purity of self and peace of mind you start your spiritual journey.

—*Swami Niranjanananda Saraswati*

Adapt, adjust, accommodate

When there is shantata the maintenance of peace, harmony and balance becomes more important than satisfying desires and demanding your rights. Swami Sivananda encapsulated this in his spiritual instruction: adapt, adjust, accommodate. This succinct instruction draws on the qualities of head, heart and hands and outlines a sadhana for the attainment of shantata. The ability to adapt is the starting point and this relates to the head. In the short-term to adapt means to alter or change something in order to make it suitable for a different purpose. When we adapt our thoughts and behaviour in order to co-operate with people and interact in different conditions and situations, a shift happens in the mind. The mental conditioning changes and understanding develops as we learn to accept the situations of life. In the long-term the word adapt describes a process of evolution. In the same way that a species can adapt, the mind and the awareness can also adapt beyond the limited selfish constraints of tamasic and rajasic conditioning to experience the spiritual dimension of life.

This second aspect is the ability to adjust and this relates to the aspect of hands and performance in life. To adjust something is to change it slightly, to modify, fix or improve upon something you already have. Developing the ability to adjust helps in shantata, because you are working with the present reality. Your effort is not to change the external situations of life, but to improve and fine-tune the responses and reactions and create something better and brighter.

This means letting go of the rigidity of ego involved in 'I know best'. Instead of doing the same thing in the same way for years and remaining stuck, adjustment influences your performance and allows the creative expression of the hands in life.

The ability to accommodate is a quality of the heart. To accommodate someone or something means you are able to make space for them in your life. It requires an open and expansive heart that is free from justification, judgement and bias. The openhearted person will always find space for someone, no matter how inconvenient. They will not dwell on what kind of facilities can be offered, and how crowded things will become, because the sentiment of love and connection dominates their reaction. If love is there then what else matters? The negative reaction of, 'No, it's not possible, there isn't enough space' hides the constriction and limitation of the selfish heart. This has to change if you want to experience shantata in life. That happens through bhava and the cultivation of positive sentiments of acceptance, friendship and love.

'Adapt, adjust, accommodate' demonstrates the difference between the development of material and spiritual awareness. In order to succeed in the material world, skills, capacity and knowledge are developed to fulfil desires, attain material goals and satisfy ambitions. This promotes a self-centred identity fuelled by the notion that even the most unrealistic personal expectations will somehow be magically fulfilled. Spiritual education emphasizes the opposite; the ability to accept the situations of life as they are, with equipoise, balance and harmony, while maintaining a state of mind saturated with inner happiness, contentment and peace. When you are at peace with yourself, you will experience the same peace everywhere, and attain a state of liberation in this world itself.

Disconnect and connect

Money cannot give you peace.
You can purchase many things, but you cannot purchase peace.
You can buy soft beds, but you cannot buy sleep.
You can buy good food, but you cannot buy good appetite.
You can buy good tonics, but you cannot buy good health.
You can buy good books, but you cannot buy wisdom.
Withdraw yourself from external objects.
Meditate and rest in your soul. You will realize everlasting peace now.

—*Swami Sivananda Saraswati*

The process begins when the connection with the material existence lessens and the spiritual awareness increases. Disconnection with the material and connection with the spiritual is a twofold process. Disconnection means withdrawing the awareness from the material world. Awareness, involvement, attachment and identification are all different mediums by which we connect with the world and as such they are also manifestations of energy. If you try to withdraw that energy from the external environment and material world without providing another focus, a vacuum is created. A positive direction needs to be given to the mental energy that has been withdrawn. That is the role of yama in lifestyle.

The positive focus given to the mind is yama. Yama is like a magnet that draws steadily towards it all the other traits and tendencies of mind. The magnetic force of the yama comes from the sattwa guna. The stronger the magnet the stronger the attraction of the positive quality in the mind, directing the awareness and energy inwards, to discover and unite with the pure inner nature. The stronger the attraction of sattwa is in the mind, the greater the ability to attract and transform the dissipated, negative vrittis and conditions of mind. It is not that krodha disappears. The instinctive reaction remains but when the vritti arises it does not disturb the balance of the mind. It is a small ripple in the otherwise tranquil waters of the mind, which quickly subsides. That is shantata.

This feeling of serenity is created when there is balance between the externalized awareness and internalized awareness. When a balance between these two develops, disconnection from the stressors of life takes place automatically and the experience of harmony develops naturally and spontaneously. When there is shantata, the faculties of head, heart and hands are in balance and the entire personality is at peace. Generally, there is total discord between the thoughts in the mind, the feelings of the heart and the method of expressing both. People feel one thing, think another and express something entirely different. This creates imbalance. To develop the experience of shantata these three components of the personality have to be unified and able to reflect a cohesive and integrated expression of consciousness. This happens through integral yoga sadhana and following the yogic precepts that support this development.

Key points for the development of shantata
- Keep a balance between external engagement and inner awareness.
- Include time for quiet contemplation in the daily routine.
- If you are externalized and active in the world for sixteen hours per day, keep one hour for the development of internal awareness.
- Maintain awareness of your thoughts, speech, action and feelings.
- Aim for harmony and simplicity in all the faculties of head, heart and hands.
- Avoid inner conflict.
- Adapt, adjust, accommodate.
- Practise japa.

You must try to remain cool even in the most provocative conditions. If you are hungry and if you suffer from any disease, you generally become more irritable. If you have some troubles, difficulties or loss, you get irritated for little things. If a sannyasi who lives in the cave says that he has controlled anger, you cannot believe him. The waves are for the time being suppressed. There are no opportunities for his getting irritated. If some transactions take place, if he is ill-treated, he will again manifest his anger. The world is a better training college for the control of anger.

If you can rest in this ocean of peace, all the usual noises of the world can hardly affect you. If you enter the silence or the wonderful calm of divine peace by stilling the bubbling mind and restraining the thoughts and withdrawing the outgoing senses, all disturbing noises will die away. Motor cars may roll on the streets; boys may shout at the pitch of their voices; railway trains may run in front of your house; several mills may be working in your neighbourhood – and yet, all these noises will not disturb you even a bit.

—*Swami Sivananda Saraswati*

NIYAMITATA

Lead a well regulated life. Proper hours of work and rest are necessary. Too much fatigue, strain of any organ and mental strain should be avoided. Stick to the happy medium. Then alone can you be peaceful and happy.

—*Swami Sivananda Saraswati*

Niyamitata is the niyama that supports the attainment of shantata. *Niyamitata* describes the attributes of regularity and practicality that help maintain balance. The state of balance and equipoise is an attribute of sattwa. Niyamitata is the practical approach to life that creates a sattwic environment conducive to balanced development at the physical, mental, emotional and spiritual levels.

In addition to balanced practicality and organization, niyamitata also involves qualities of personality that need to be developed. These qualities help establish niyamitata in life. A description of niyamitata given in the *Yoga Sutras* of Patanjali describes the conditions necessary for the success of sadhana (1.14):

स तु दीर्घकाल नैरन्तर्य सत्कारादरासेवितो दृढभूमिः ॥

Sah tu dirgha kala nairantaira satkara asevitah dridha bhumih.

It becomes firmly grounded by being continued for a long time with reverence, without interruption.

As a lifestyle niyama, niyamitata is the sadhana of lifestyle, and this description given by Patanjali helps identify the different qualities to develop in order to progress. Two qualities of niyamitata relate to time, *dirghakala*, meaning for a long time and *nairantarya*, or continuously, without interruption. The routine you decide upon should be maintained, continuously, without break and continue for an extended duration. It will not work to start a new routine every third day because you cannot maintain it.

The next aspects relate to the *bhava* or attitude to cultivate. This is *satkara*, the attitude of seriousness, care, devotion, and *adara*, reverence and respect. Finally, the mental attitude described by *asevito* implies the dedication to follow and cultivate with assiduous attention. To develop niyamitata in life, try to enhance these qualities. When these attributes are present, the basis for your niyamitata practice will be sound and well founded.

Niyamitata also follows the practice of indriya nigraha in a spontaneous and natural progression in lifestyle. By practising indriya nigraha, you learn how unrestrained sensorial input affects the mind and influences the personality. When the senses and mind are observed through the lens of the gunas, the understanding of the different kinds of influences on the mind and personality becomes precise. Exposure to food, people, routine and environments that are tamasic have a corresponding influence on the mind, making it deluded, self-absorbed and weighed down by negativity. Exposure to rajasic conditions excite, dissipate and agitate the mind, and the aggressive, reactive, selfish and egotistical patterns increase. If the external influences are regulated and balanced, there are less distractions and dissipation. Indriya nigraha becomes spontaneous when the outer environment and interactions are regulated, balanced and practical. The inclination towards the sattwic conditions of life naturally develops, because sensorial input that is sattwic brings peace.

Niyamitata is the regular performance of action that generates the condition and experience of sattwa. In contrast to the binding force of tamas that impedes positivity and the passionate aggressive drive of rajas, the nature of sattwa is wisdom and effulgence. Niyamitata is the proper organization of the simple daily routine that brings light, understanding and happiness to life. This is the basis of spiritual life and is seen in the lives of saints and sages throughout the ages who have lived simply, maintaining the correct and appropriate balance despite changing circumstances. Niyamitata is the balance between individual needs and the environment, between individual desires and the greater good, and between the disciplined effort of sadhana and the effortless flow of surrender and grace.

Desire and anger are our greatest enemies. If you want to gain victory over them, always engage yourself in work.

—*Swami Satyananda Saraswati*

As modern society moves further away from the natural cycles and severs the connection between humans and nature, lifestyle has become the main cause of imbalance. Nature and all of created life depend on sustained regularity for existence. Day and night, the sun and moon, seasons and tides, all follow a regular pattern and a rhythm of regularity creating the symphony of life. When this regularity is disturbed, there is chaos, fear and insecurity. Human beings are no exception to this rule. If lifestyle is irregular and disordered, there is chaos at the physical, mental and emotional levels, and spirituality is impossible.

Moderation and routine
Looking at niyamitata from the lifestyle perspective there are many components that can be fine-tuned in order to develop niyamitata. The first two areas of focus are moderation and routine. Moderation means avoiding the extremes and the excesses in life. Extremes in lifestyle create imbalance in the mind, while moderation creates balance and security. Routine means doing the right thing at the right time, within a system of consolidation or repetition. A proper routine brings security and peace to life. These two attributes are also seen in the natural biological rhythm of the human body.

When it is dark at night the eyes send a signal to the hypothalamus that it is time to feel tired. The brain in turn begins to secrete melatonin and the feeling of drowsiness begins. In a regular cycle melatonin levels rise in the evening, peak overnight and then start to drop by morning, supporting the sleep patterns that follow the natural cycle. Over the 24-hour period the body follows the circadian rhythm influencing the sleep and wake cycle, as well as hormone release, body temperature and metabolism. The nature and condition of the body has a vital effect upon the mind and the vrittis. An imbalanced routine that emphasizes activities after dark, staying up late, eating late and increased exposure to artificial lighting is detrimental to body, mind and emotions. A proper routine of sleeping, exercising, eating and interacting are the first aspects of niyamitata.

Maintaining regular sleeping patterns that ensure adequate hours of sleep is essential. However, non-REM sleep that is deeper and more restorative tends to dominate the cycles in the early part of the night. Towards daybreak the REM cycles predominate, and the restorative quality of sleep lessens. It is better to sleep early and rise early. Poor and insufficient sleep is linked to negativity and increases the likelihood that people will interpret the circumstances of life in a negative way. Consistent healthy sleeping patterns are also important in maintaining serotonin functioning in the brain and body, helping to prevent and manage the reactions of krodha. Sleep deprivation desensitizes serotonin pathways, which means that consistent lack of sleep has a negative impact on the brain's response to serotonin in general. This in turn exacerbates the reaction of krodha.

Additionally, exercise can increase the production of endorphins, which are known to help produce positive feelings and reduce the perception of pain. Regular exercise has been shown to reduce symptoms in people suffering from anxiety, promoting a more objective awareness. Interestingly, it doesn't matter how intense your workout is. It seems that your mood can benefit from exercise no matter the intensity of the physical activity. Regular physical activity can help you fall asleep faster, get better sleep and deepen your sleep.

The average to aim for is about 30 minutes of moderate exercise daily. If this is done at the time of sunrise or sunset, then the promotion of circadian rhythms is an additional bonus. Increases in daily activity can come from small changes made throughout your day, such as walking or cycling instead of using the car, getting off a tram, train or bus a stop earlier and walking the rest of the way, or walking the children to school.

Exercise is also an essential component of a balanced routine for mind and body. Regular exercise is not only important for physical health, but it also boosts the levels of serotonin in both blood and brain, offsetting the chemical imbalance of krodha.

Food

Developing niyamitata not only applies to establishing a routine of eating that is in harmony with the natural cycle of the body, it also relates to the type of food that we eat. There is a direct relationship between krodha and food intake and this is not only experienced at the physiological level, but also the mental levels. Regular mealtimes are necessary to ensure the correct flow of serotonin that maintains neuronal balance. Due to low serotonin levels, krodha is more likely when you are hungry and more difficult to control. One of the best ways to begin management of krodha is to ensure regular mealtimes. Eat the right food at the right time.

Everything in the realm of prakriti is constituted and conditioned by the three gunas and food is no exception. The food we consume is either tamasic, rajasic or sattwic and accordingly has a different effect on the body, brain and mind. You can assess a person's nature according to the particular food they prefer. A sattwic person will eat khichari. A rajasic person will want oily paratha and spicy sabjee or vegetables. A tamasic person will eat last night's paratha for breakfast! Desire for certain types of food also has its origin in the guna that is predominant at the time. In

137

a tamasic mood, tamasic food will be consumed. When rajas is dominant the craving will be for rajasic food.

To attain and experience mental balance and harmony, the foods that build the body and the mind should be pure. The subtlest essence of food is assimilated by the mind. Ideas, concepts, thinking patterns and attitudes are all generated in the mind in correspondence to the food that is eaten. Sattwic food is easily assimilated and absorbed and promotes purity, strength, vitality and health. It is fresh and juicy and the sight of it produces cheerfulness, serenity and mental clarity. Milk, butter, fresh seasonal fruits and grains are all sattwic. Sattwic food not only sustains the physical body, it is also a supply of positive mental energy and connects the mind with happiness and joy.

Sattwic food promotes cheerfulness, serenity and mental clarity and helps the aspirant enter into meditation, maintain mental peace and nervous equilibrium. There is an intimate connection between the body and the mind. The nature and condition of the body has a vital effect upon the mind and activities. Therefore, the materials or foods that build the body should be pure, wholesome, nutritious, substantial and bland.

—*Swami Sivananda Saraswati*

To practise niyamitata, avoid food that is tamasic and rajasic. Tamasic food has a dulling nature. It promotes lethargy, illness, impurity and disease. Tamasic food includes everything that is processed, filled with chemical additives and preservatives. It does not supply nutrients and sustenance. Everything stale, rotten, overcooked, and putrid is tamasic. Tamasic food increases the experience and expression of tamasic krodha. Rajasic foods agitate the body, mind and prana. It is food that has a passionate nature and produces the corresponding mental experiences of restlessness, negative destructive thoughts, desire, craving, pain and disease. Rajasic food is excessively bitter, sour, salty, hot, pungent or spicy. Fried foods, onions, garlic, tea, coffee, meat, fish, eggs, okra, eggplant, lemon, chilies are all rajasic. Caffeine is rajasic and it triggers the release of adrenaline.

Proper and regulated intake of fluid is also required to maintain the proper functioning of the body as well as mental and emotional balance. Pure water is the most sattwic fluid. Avoid drinks that are high in caffeine, sugar, chemicals and preservatives. These create extreme spikes of reaction in the constitution and disrupt the natural cycles of the body and prana. Water is also an aid to the management of krodha. Swami Sivananda advocated drinking cool water whenever irritation or anger was felt. Krodha is related to the *agni tattwa*, the fire element, and creates heat in the body. *Apas*, or water, is the element to pacify and neutralize agni. You don't cry tears when you are angry, but you may cry in the aftermath of an argument or hostile encounter. This is the natural effect of water to dampen the fire of agni, restore balance and heal the damage of krodha.

Sweet speech

After regulation of sleep, exercise and diet that brings a level of physical, mental and emotional balance, the next aspect of niyamitata is a practical approach to daily communication and interaction. This area of life is a major trigger of krodha and yet it is generally overlooked in management of routine and lifestyle. The major vehicle for the expression of krodha is through speech. Harsh speech, arguments and verbal retaliation are the vehicles of krodha that intensify the expression of the vritti and cause untold harm to others. The worst of arguments leave the person wishing they could take back what was said in the heat of the moment. The different styles and intensity of that expression is endless, but whether it is sarcastic remarks and criticism, or outright insult and abuse, the power of the spoken word to cause pain and anguish is immense.

From the yogic perspective, regulation and balance of speech is an austerity or *tapasya* in its own right. Unres-

139

trained, aggressive and destructive speech, that unleashes the full power of the negative mind upon another person, can reduce all the achievements of sadhana to naught. For this reason, the effort to control and regulate what is spoken is an important component of any spiritual sadhana and lifestyle. Such is the power of the spoken word. By regulating speech, you are restraining the expression and managing the experience of krodha. When you begin to imbibe and express the principles of niyamitata through speech, not only are the destructive influence of tamas and rajas transformed, but the connection to the qualities of sattwa deepens and becomes part of your nature.

The organ of speech causes great distraction of mind. Control of speech is a difficult discipline but you will have to practise it if you want to attain supreme peace.

—*Swami Sivananda Saraswati*

In the *Bhagavad Gita* Sri Krishna holds speech that is truthful, pleasant and beneficial and which does not cause excitement, pain or agitation as the tapasya or austerity of speech. This leads one towards the expression and experience of sattwa. In the *Manu Smriti* similarly it is said that one should speak that which is true and that which is pleasant. One should not speak that which is true if it is not pleasant, nor what is pleasant if it is false. The principles of niyamitata provide similar guidelines. Moderate speech does not cause pain, it is pleasant and truthful. Using the right words at the right time and not saying the wrong at the wrong time, is following an appropriate routine and regulation of speech. This is the beginning of ahimsa and the transformation of krodha.

The words of the man who practises the austerity of speech cannot cause pain to others. His words will bring cheer and solace to others. His words will prove beneficial to all. The organ of speech causes great distraction of mind. Control of speech is a difficult discipline but you will have to practise it if you want to attain supreme peace.

—Swami Sivananda Saraswati

Key points for the development of niyamitata

- Aim to bring your daily routine in harmony with the natural circadian rhythm that follows the sun.
- Rise early and sleep early.
- Get plenty of sleep. Between 7 to 9 hours is the general requirement for adults.
- Increase your exposure to natural light in the daytime and avoid unnatural light especially blue light from screens (TV, phones, ipads) at night.
- Eat at regular intervals, preferably at the same time every day.
- Eat more during the day than you eat at night and finish the evening meal ideally one to two hours before sleep.
- Incorporate more sattwic foods into the diet and decrease intake of tamasic and rajasic foods.
- Some foods with high levels of serotonin are walnuts, plantains, pineapples, bananas, kiwifruit and tomatoes. One of the most important vitamins key to serotonin function is thiamine, one of the components of Vitamin B Complex.
- Drink water regularly and ensure the body is properly hydrated. When you feel irritated or frustrated, drink a glass of cool water.
- Maintain one hour of mouna, silence, every day.
- Speak softly. Speak sweetly. Do not cause harm or pain through your speech.

Whenever there is a little irritability, stop all conversation and observe mouna, silence. The practice of mouna daily for one or two hours is of great help in controlling anger. Always try to speak sweet, soft words. The words must be soft and the arguments hard; but if the reverse is the case it will lead to discord and disharmony. There is a sharp sword in every tongue.

An aspirant should direct all his attention towards the conquest of this powerful enemy, krodha. Sattwic food, japa, regular meditation, prayer, satsang, service, vichara, kirtan, practice of pranayama and Brahmacharya – all are some of the most potent factors that pave a long way in eradicating this dire malady. A combined method should be adopted in its eradication. Smoking, meat eating and drinking of liquors make men very irritable. Therefore, these should be completely abandoned. Be careful in the choice of your company. Give up the companionship of negative characters. Talk little. Mix little. Plunge yourself into the spiritual sadhana. Develop *kshama*, forgiveness, *vishwaprema*, cosmic love, *karuna*, mercy, and *nirabhimanata*, absence of egoism.

—*Swami Sivananda Saraswati*

10

Transforming Krodha through Ahimsa

The one message of all saints and prophets of all times and climes, is the message of love, *ahimsa*, of selfless service. Ahimsa is the noblest and best of traits that are found expressed in the daily life and activities of perfected souls. Ahimsa is the one means, not only to attain salvation, but also to enjoy uninterrupted peace and bliss.

—*Swami Sivananda Saraswati*

Ahimsa is a beautiful concept and condition of mind. Ahimsa is not only non-violence or refraining from harm. Ahimsa is a quality that comes from a state of pure love and goodness. Anyone, even in the most difficult situation and circumstance of life can draw on the immense power and radiant spiritual luminosity of ahimsa. Acts and expressions of ahimsa are a shining light that can illumine any darkness and inspire all those who are a witness to them. The choice to do the right and righteous, to be good and do good, is ever present, in every moment of life. We have the choice to speak softly, support and encourage, or berate, belittle and destroy. We have the choice to express affection and love, or we can spit venom and spite.

Himsa, harm or violence, is the power that poisons and destroys life. Ahimsa is the power that sustains. Think about your own life. It is the goodwill and generous nature of other people that has fed, nurtured and sustained you from infancy until today. To live without kindness, love, sympathy and support is no life at all. If at all we could survive the isolation, it would be a grim and miserable struggle. Yet we thrive when there is love, compassion and understanding. Ahimsa is pure, universal, cosmic love. It is the development of a mental attitude in which all forms of hatred are replaced by love. Ahimsa is true sacrifice, strength and forgiveness. The practice of ahimsa is the practice of love that leads to the experience of *atmabhava*, feeling oneness with all beings.

> The practice of ahimsa develops love. Ahimsa is another name for truth or love. Ahimsa is universal love. It is pure love. It is divine prem. Where there is love, there you will find ahimsa. Where there is ahimsa, there you will find love and selfless service. They all go together. No self-realization is possible without ahimsa. It is through the practice of ahimsa alone that you can cognize and reach the Supreme Self or Brahman.
>
> —*Swami Sivananda Saraswati*

Raja yoga sadhana

There are two different sadhanas for the development of ahimsa. The first is often explained within the context of raja yoga, due to the inclusion of ahimsa as a yama by Patanjali. Here the emphasis is on individual practice and the restraint of negativity leading to purification of the mind and emotions. The focus is threefold: restraint of thought, word and deed. When explaining this sadhana in his writings Swami Sivananda encouraged aspirants to start with control of the physical body because it is easier to control than the mind, and as the first step, refrain from causing any physical harm.

Once the physical reactions are under control, from the body you move the awareness to speech and try to eliminate any harsh and unkind speech. No harm or injury should be caused to anyone through the medium of speech. This

144

does not mean that the person must hear what is said directly, himsa is also lying, gossiping, speaking ill of others, backbiting or vilifying. Even if you are not the one speaking, even listening to or endorsing and approving of criticism of another is himsa. Non-verbal communication is also included in this stage of sadhana, including wounding the feelings of others by gesture, expression, or tone of voice.

Finally, the very thought of himsa has to be restrained and removed from the mental field. This is not only the thought of violence or harm; it refers to the entire spectrum of dwesha and negativity. Anything from condescension to entertaining unreasonable dislike for or prejudice towards anybody, harbouring thoughts of hatred, malice, contempt, delighting in another's misfortune or jealousy is himsa. This is the basic sadhana for the development of ahimsa, control and restraint of the negative manifestations and expressions of thought, word and deed.

However, Swami Sivananda has given a clue to the progression of this initial sadhana, because he extends ahimsa beyond simply restraining the negative expression or mentality. Ahimsa is not only restraining negativity, it is also positive and constructive action. It is not enough to do no harm, you should also be good and do good. It is himsa when you fail to perform the correct and appropriate action. It is himsa when you do not say what should be said, and when your thoughts do not reflect what is appropriate and correct. Witnessing cruelty and not doing anything is himsa. Seeing someone being bullied and not helping them is himsa. Seeing the pain of others and not responding, by not giving aid when needed is himsa.

> You may be in quite adverse circumstances. You may remain in the midst of calamities, troubles, tribulations, difficulties and sorrows, and yet, you may enjoy the inward harmony and peace if you rest in God by withdrawing the senses, by stilling the mind and eradicating its impurities. Lord Jesus was persecuted in

a variety of ways. He was put to death on the cross and yet what did he say? He said, "O Lord, forgive them! They know not what they do." How peaceful He was even when His life was at stake! He was enjoying the inner peace.

Ahimsa is soul force. Hate melts in the presence of love. Hate dissolves in the presence of ahimsa. There is no greater power than ahimsa. The power of ahimsa is infinitely more wonderful and subtler than electricity or magnetism. The law of ahimsa is as exact and precise as the law of gravitation or cohesion. You must know the correct way to apply it intelligently and with scientific accuracy. If you are able to apply it with exactitude and precision, you can work wonders.

—*Swami Sivananda Saraswati*

Sadhana for ahimsa given by Swami Sivananda

First, control your physical body. Suppress your feelings. Follow the instructions of Jesus Christ in his Sermon on the Mount:

> If a man beats you on one cheek, turn to him the other cheek also.
>
> If a man takes away your coat, give him your shirt also.

This is very difficult in the beginning. The old *samskaras*, impressions, of revenge, of 'a tooth for a tooth', 'an eye for an eye', and 'paying in the same coin' will all force you to retaliate. You will have to wait coolly. Reflect and meditate. Do *vichara* or right enquiry. The mind will become calm. The opponent who was very furious will also become calm, because he does not get any opposition from your side. He gets astonished and terrified also, because you stand like a sage. By and by, you will gain immense strength. Keep the ideal before you. Try to get at it, though with faltering steps at first. Have a clear-cut mental image of ahimsa and its immeasurable advantages.

After controlling the body, control your speech. Make a strong determination, 'I will not speak any harsh word to anybody from today'. You may fail a hundred times. What does it matter? You will slowly gain strength. Check the impulse of speech. Observe *mouna*, silence. Practise *kshama* or forgiveness. Say within yourself, 'He is a baby-soul. He is ignorant, that is why he has done it. Let me excuse him this time. What do I gain by abusing him in return?' Slowly give up *abhimana*, ego-centred attachment. Abhimana is the root-cause of human sufferings.

Finally, go to the thoughts and check the thought of injuring. Never even think of injuring anyone. One Self dwells in all. All are manifestations of One God. By injuring another, you injure your own Self. By serving another, you serve your own Self. Love all. Serve all. Hate none. Insult none. Injure none in thought, word and deed. Try to behold your own Self in all beings.

Vedantic sadhana

For most people ahimsa remains limited to the raja yoga approach of restraint. Yet this is only the first stage, the preparatory practices towards purification of mind and the attainment of ahimsa. The second stage in which you experience and live ahimsa begins where the first stage ends. In the first stage, the effort is to restrain and moderate your thoughts and behaviour. However, in the second stage, you try to expand the range of awareness and deepen the experience of yourself, not only as an individual but also in relation to the world. It is an experiential process, a systematic expansion and merger of sequential stages of realization. This vedantic sadhana evolves naturally through the progression of lifestyle yama and niyama.

Both namaskara and kshama work by expanding the awareness beyond the self-oriented orbit that keeps the mind bound to the material dimension of life. Namaskara begins with recognition of others and developing a sentiment of goodwill towards all, no matter in what circumstance or station of life. By practising kshama you lay the foundation for ahimsa. When thoughts of revenge and hatred arise in the mind, forgiveness is the way out of the maze of negativity that leads you beyond the urge to retaliate. If you faithfully practise for some months, negative thoughts of revenge have no scope of manifestation and die by themselves. More importantly, kshama uses your own feelings of suffering, hurt and resentment to develop an understanding of how other people feel when treated rudely, with disrespect and hostility.

First bhumika

In the Vedantic sadhana, the initial experience is a self-oriented awareness of your own suffering. The first step towards living ahimsa happens when you can expand your individual experience to include other people. You understand that other people also feel hurt and pain in the same way. Just as you do not wish to feel pain and sadness and would rather be happy, the other person also shares the same desire, to be happy and avoid suffering. Here is the first *bhumika* or foundation. The understanding and experience of unity in diversity.

> To fail to relieve another's pain, or even to neglect to go to the person in distress is a sort of himsa. It is the sin of omission. Avoid strictly all forms of harshness, direct or indirect, positive or negative, immediate or delayed. Practise ahimsa in its purest form and become divine. Ahimsa and Divinity are one.
>
> —*Swami Sivananda Saraswati*

From this realization, the state of ahimsa flows naturally into life. You live in a different appreciation and understanding of yourself in relation to the world and the environment. From the material perspective, people are different, different colours, different bodies, minds, feelings and experiences, but from the spiritual perspective, in essence we are the same. Individual ambitions and desires remain, but they are understood within a broader perspective. You do not hurt or harm other people because you recognize that you also do not wish to be hurt. You do not feel separate from others and isolated because there is an underlying experience of connection that sustains and enriches life.

Second bhumika

The second bhumika of ahimsa is atmabhava, the ability to see and experience yourself in others. In the beginning, this is based on a deeper understanding and enhanced empathy. Swami Satyananda has spoken of atmabhava as the true test of Vedanta. Atmabhava is not just thinking 'I am Brahman, you are Brahman'. It has to be more than an intellectual understanding. Atmabhava has to be felt. How is this possible? Through the expansion of awareness. Awareness has to expand to encompass not only your own suffering but also that of others. Here is the possibility to feel the suffering of another as if it were your own.

> Spiritual life begins by itself when you experience atmabhava.
> —*Swami Satyananda Saraswati*

Third bhumika

It is in the third bhumika that we find the positive expression of ahimsa given in the teachings of Swami Sivananda. In the third bhumika living ahimsa moves beyond simply refraining from harm to actively cultivating the good and the positive in life. It is now that the positive component of ahimsa emerges. If you experience someone else's suffering as keenly as you feel your own, the inclination to remove that suffering spontaneously manifests. You want to help. If someone is cold, you want to give blankets. If someone is sick, you will make sure the correct medicine is given. At this level the sadhana is simple: be good and do good. The attainment of ahimsa is seen in the aspect of being good. The expression of that attainment is seen in the aspect of doing good. This is not only *seva*, selfless service, it is the practical expression of ahimsa.

It is not just a question of understanding the mental states in meditation. One has to make the effort to bring that higher realization into the daily activities. That realization manifests in the form of refined qualities, refined behaviour and interaction with the world and a deep understanding. When we have these qualities in our life and we are experiencing them, then that state is similar to the state of realization. This spiritual realization is the system of Vedanta where one does not only relate to a state of experience intellectually, one lives it.

—*Swami Niranjanananda Saraswati*

11

Hints for Control of Anger

Swami Sivananda Saraswati

1. Be alert. Pray. Do more japa. Practise vichara. Keep a watch over your mind. Be silent. Observe mouna daily for an hour. Forget and forgive. Bear insult and injury. Observe Brahmacharya.
2. See God in all. Submit to God's will. Then you cannot get angry.
3. In the morning meditate on the virtue of patience. Manifest it during the day. Take a vow 'I will practise endurance and kshama, forgiveness, during the day'.
4. Speak sweetly. Speak little.
5. Mix little. Have congenial company. Have satsang. Read spiritual books.
6. Remember the lives of saints like Eknath, the Avanti Brahmin of the eleventh Skandha of the *Bhagavata*. You will derive inspiration. You will develop love and kshama.
7. Give up intoxicating liquors, meat and tobacco.
8. Remember the *Gita* slokas 3:37 and 16:21, describing anger as a monster and gate to hell.
9. If you find it difficult to control anger, leave the place at once. Take a long walk. Drink cold water. Repeat *Om Shanti* ten times. Do japa of your Ishta mantra or count from 1 to 30. Anger will subside.

10. Stand as a witness of the vritti of anger. Be indifferent to it. Do not identify yourself with it. Identify yourself with the Atman. Fill the mind with ideas of love, joy, etc.

11. Develop patience to a considerable extent. People lose their temper when they become impatient. Allow the mind to dwell constantly on the opposite of anger, the virtue of patience. This is the pratipaksha bhavana method of raja yogins.

12. Do not give vent to anger. Control the body first. Have physical control. Practise this again and again. Be regular in your japa, meditation and kirtan. This will give you great inner spiritual strength.

13. Food has a great deal to do with irritability. Take milk, fruits, moong-ki-dal, curd, spinach, barley, groundnuts, butter milk. Do not take carrots, onion, garlic, cauliflower, massoor-ki-dal and drumstick.

14. Observe mouna for two hours daily. Occasionally observe mouna for a whole day. This will put a check on the impulse of speech. When a man gets excited, he speaks anything and everything. He has no control over the organ of speech.

15. Prana entwines the mind like a creeper. Pranayama leads to the control of mind. Pranayama will put a break on the

impulse of speech. It will give you abundant energy to check anger.

16. Do not argue much. Do not retort. Speak sweetly always. Do not use abusive words. Become a man of measured words. If a man abuses or insults you, keep quiet. Identify yourself with Atman. Atman is the same in all. It can never be hurt or insulted.

17. A Vedantin denies the body and mind as illusory sheaths. He does vichara, enquires, 'who am I' and practises *neti-neti* – 'not this, not this'. 'I am not the body'. 'I am not the mind', *Chidanandaroopa Shivoham* – 'I am blissful Shiva or Atman'. He identifies himself with Brahman or Atman, the Eternal. The world is unreal for him. He chants *Om*, sings *Om* and does japa of *Om* and meditates on *Om* and derives soul-power and spiritual strength.

18. If you entertain mithya drishti and dosha drishti, a false and impure view, if you look into the defects of anger and the benefits of patience, you will never become angry.

19. The combined method is more effective. If one method fails, take recourse to the combined method. Do japa, pranayama. Sometimes do vichara.

12

Six-month Sadhana Capsule

The six friends disrupt the harmony and the flow of energy in the mind. They divert the inner attention from the goal that you have in front of you. The goal is the experience of the three conditions of life: *satyam*, truth; *shivam*, auspicious nature; and *sundaram*, beauty, which you can appreciate and incorporate in your own lifestyle. The purpose of yoga is to come to this point of total experience: the experience of truth, the experience of everything uplifting, positive and auspicious, and the experience and awareness of the beauty that surrounds you. This is the purpose of yoga.

—*Swami Niranjanananda Saraswati*

A six-month sadhana capsule is given here to help aspirants work systematically and progressively through the gunas in the effort to transform krodha.

MONTH 1 AND 2

Hatha yoga
Asana: sadhana as given
Pranayama: sheetali or sheetkari, bhramari, ujjayi
Mudra: shambhavi
Shatkarma: neti once a week

Jnana yoga
SWAN weekly:
Identify the weakness that catalyzes krodha. Then
identify one strength to counteract the weakness
Review of the Day every night

Raja yoga
Yoga nidra daily
Indriya nigraha daily

Lifestyle sadhana
Namaskara:
1. Make the effort to greet the people you know with
positivity and joy.
2. Connect with and express the positive aspects of your
nature.
3. Complete the questionnaire weekly (second month).

Kshama:
1. Take a sankalpa to forgive one perceived wrong from your
past.
2. Make the effort to release the past and live in the present.
3. Complete the questionnaire weekly (second month).

Niyamitata:
1. Implement two key points for the development of
niyamitata in the first month.

The root cause of anger is ignorance and egoism. Through *vichara*, right enquiry, egoism should be removed. Then alone can one control his anger completely. Through development of the opposite virtues such as forgiveness, peace, compassion, friendship, love, anger can be controlled to an enormous degree. The force can be reduced. *Atmajnana*, knowledge of the self, alone can fry all samskaras of anger and eradicate it in toto.

—*Swami Sivananda Saraswati*

MONTH 3 AND 4

Hatha yoga
   Asana: sadhana as given
   Pranayama: sheetali or sheetkari, bhramari, nadi shodhana
   Mudra: shambhavi, nasikagra
   Shatkarma: neti once a week, kunjal once every two weeks

Jnana yoga
   SWAN weekly:
      Identify one ambition that catalyzes krodha.
      Develop understanding of your needs to counter
      ambitions. Discriminate between need and ambition.
   Review of the Day every night
   Pratipaksha bhavana

Raja yoga
   Yoga nidra daily
   Danti daily

Lifestyle sadhana

Namaskara:
1. Make the effort to greet the people you know with
   positivity and joy.
2. Connect with and express the positive aspects of your
   nature.
3. Practise namaskara with all, regardless of status or
   position.
4. Develop the feeling and/or understanding of the unity
   and equality of all.
5. Complete the questionnaire weekly (second month).

Kshama:
1. Take a sankalpa to forgive one perceived wrong from your
   past.
2. Make the effort to release the past and live in the present.

3. Develop an awareness of the hurt your behaviour has caused in the past
4. Mentally seek forgiveness for harm that you have caused.
5. Complete the questionnaire weekly (second month)

Niyamitata:
1. Implement two key points for the development of niyamitata.

Shantata:
1. Develop the ability to flow with life.
2. Adapt, adjust, accommodate.

If you understand the doctrine of unity in variety, if you know there is only one matter, one energy, one mind-substance, one life, one existence, one reality, and if you entertain always such a thought, you can control krodha. If you remember that you are only an instrument in the hands of God, that God is everything, God does everything, God is just, then you can get rid of ahamkara. You can annihilate dwesha by pratipaksha bhavana. Look to the brighter side of persons. Ignore the dark aspect.

—*Swami Sivananda Saraswati*

MONTHS 5 AND 6

Hatha yoga
- Asana: sadhana as given
- Pranayama: bhramari, nadi shodhana
- Mudra: shambhavi, nasikagra, shanmukhi
- Shatkarma: laghoo shankaprakshalana

Jnana yoga
- Review of the Day every night
- Pratipaksha bhavana

Raja yoga
- Yoga nidra daily
- Danti daily first month

Maintain your lifestyle sadhana
Namaskara:
1. Make the effort to greet the people you know with positivity and joy.
2. Connect with and express the positive aspects of your nature.
3. Practise namaskara with all, regardless of status or position.
4. Develop the feeling and/or understanding of the unity and equality of all.
5. Complete the questionnaire weekly.

Kshama:
1. Take a sankalpa to forgive one perceived wrong from your past.
2. Make the effort to release the past and live in the present.
3. Develop an awareness of the hurt your behaviour has caused in the past.
4. Mentally seek forgiveness for harm that you have caused.
5. Complete the questionnaire weekly.

Niyamitata:
1. Implement the remaining key points for the development of niyamitata.

Shantata:
1. Develop the ability to flow with life.
2. Adapt, adjust, accommodate.
3. Find a balance between internal and external awareness.
4. Harmonize the expressions of head, heart and hands.

Ahimsa:
1. Raja yoga sadhana for ahimsa in the first month
2. Vedantic sadhana for ahimsa in the second month

The six friends disrupt the harmony and the flow of energy in the mind. They divert the inner attention from the goal that you have in front of you. The goal is the experience of the three conditions of life: satyam, truth; shivam, auspicious nature; and sundaram, beauty, which you can appreciate and incorporate in your own lifestyle. The purpose of yoga is to come to this point of total experience: the experience of truth, the experience of everything uplifting, positive and auspicious, and the experience and awareness of the beauty that surrounds you. This is the purpose of yoga.

—*Swami Niranjanananda Saraswati*

13

Questionnaire

YAMA OF KSHAMA – FORGIVENESS

1. How forgiving would you say you are? Rate between 1 and 10.
2. Bring to mind one situation from the past when you were not forgiving. To what extent are you holding on to it – strong, medium, weak?
3. What is the experience of krodha that memory generates in you? Frustration, resentment, bitterness, revenge?
4. Analyze this feeling to identify and try to understand the root cause of the experience of krodha. Was it disappointment, fear, a feeling of being threatened, or perhaps your self-image, self-identification and status were challenged?
5. What are your thoughts about the other person in this situation?
6. Analyze how this pattern of thought keeps you tied to the past, and reinforces the negativity in your own mind. Make a sankalpa to let go of your inner negativity by practising kshama.
7. Consciously change your negative thoughts towards the person by focusing on their positive qualities. How successful are you? Rate yourself and see if the rating improves over a period of time.

8. Bring in the thought of forgiveness and try to forgive the other person. Do you find this easy or difficult? Be objective.
9. Take the experience of forgiveness into your heart and allow it to expand. After doing this, do you feel happy, can you smile at the thought of the person, and are you ready to meet them with a hearty namaskara?

NIYAMA OF NAMASKARA – GREETING

1. Did you remember to practise namaskara sadhana today?
2. To how many people did you offer greetings today – approximately?
3. Did you do it as just a social greeting or did you do it with *bhava*, feeling?
4. If there was a bhava, what was it?
5. What was the connection you made with your inner positivity through namaskara. Were you able to overcome feelings of insecurity or arrogance?
6. Were you able to maintain that connection with inner positivity? If not, why not?
7. Did you follow Swami Sivananda's precept of doing namaskara as recognition of the divine, or the inherent goodness, in another person?
8. Were there different bhavas with different people? If yes, find out what your spontaneous response to different people is.
9. Can you make a resolve to have the same bhava of 'greeting the goodness' with everyone and try to practise it? You can rate the success of your practice over a period of time.
10. Can you notice any positive change in your overall attitude or level of respect towards others after one week, one month, or one year of practice?

Notes